MILLER'S Rock & Pop
MEMORABILIA

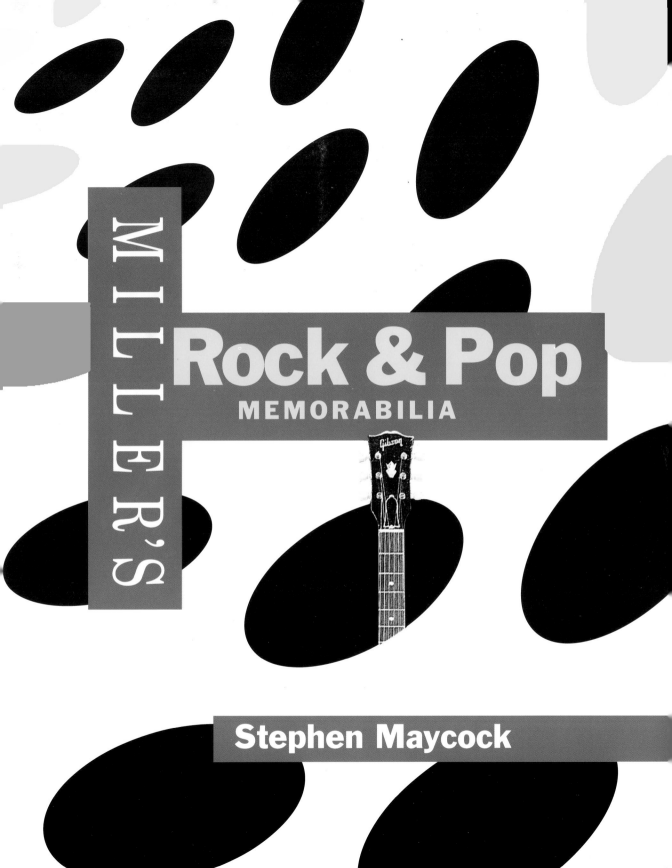

MILLER'S

Rock & Pop

MEMORABILIA

Stephen Maycock

To Georgina, Sarah and Louisa

Miller's Rock and Pop Memorabilia
Stephen Maycock

First published in Great Britain in 1994
by Miller's
an imprint of Reed Consumer Books Limited
Michelin House, 81 Fulham Road
London SW3 6RB
and Auckland, Melbourne, Singapore and Toronto

Series Editor Alison Starling
Editor Alison Macfarlane
Art Editor Mark Winwood
Production Heather O'Connell
Index Hilary Bird
Special Photography Ian Booth

A CIP catalogue record for this book is available from
the British Library

ISBN 1 85732 270 3

Set in A Garamond and Univers Condensed
Origination by Scantrans Pte Ltd, Singapore
Produced by Mandarin Offset
Printed and bound in China

Jacket Illustrations
Front cover: (Clockwise) Elvis Presley's 78rpm single *That's All
Right* on the Sun Label; a psychedelic poster for The Jimi
Hendrix Experience; a painted composition money box in the
form of George Harrison, 1968; A Gibson Les Paul Standard
guitar, signed by Jimmy Page in 1991; Keith Moon's Premier
bass drum with The Who logo on the front, c.1968.
Back cover: David Bowie's album, *The Man Who Sold The
World*, Mercury Records, 1971, with the rare "dress" cover; a
pair of Elton John's jewel-encrusted spectacles.
Back flap: A celluloid from The Beatles' *Yellow Submarine*.
p.1-3 Various cells from *The Yellow Submarine*.

Contents

Introduction

The influence of rock music on the lives of the post-war generations has been so extensive that it was perhaps only a matter of time before the collecting of rock and pop memorabilia became a formally recognized phenomenon. Arguably, the rock and pop collecting boom began in December 1981, when Sotheby's auction house in London held the first-ever sale dedicated to the subject. Two pianos belonging to Paul McCartney and John Lennon were offered to the auctioneers, and the sale grew to some 200 lots which were sold for a (then) breathtaking total of £110,000. Interest in this first rock and pop auction from both the public and the media was so intense that it was standing-room only in the saleroom. Almost overnight the rock and pop market had come into focus, and within a few years all the leading London auctioneers were holding similar sales, with unusual or expensive items regularly hitting the headlines. Such sales are now an established part of the auction calendar in London, New York, Los Angeles and San Francisco.

The collecting of rock and pop memorabilia is certainly not a new phenomenon, and music-related items have been collected by fans since the emergence of rock and roll in the 1950s. Up until 1981 purchases could be made only through classified advertisements, record fairs, fan club networks or by trading and swapping via personal contacts. Although these outlets still play a major part in the sale of rock and pop memorabilia, auction houses provide a high-profile forum from which the rarer and more valuable items can be exposed to collectors around the world.

The question often arises as to who buys this material. In the past much media coverage has been given to the considerable sums spent by various restaurant outlets for such items. The well-known restaurant chain, the Hard Rock Café, has amassed an impressive collection which functions almost as a museum. However, the majority of collectors are individuals who are simply rock and roll fans with a passion for the subject, and it is to these fans that this book is addressed, helping them to find and assess the memorabilia that they want.

By looking through the pages of this book it is not difficult to see that the market, in almost every area of rock and pop collecting, is dominated by The Beatles. Just as they dominated the world of popular music in the 1960s, their position in the world of collecting seems unassailable. Items relating to the group or to individual members frequently command record prices, and John Lennon's name in particular appears time and again in the list of the most expensive pieces of rock and pop memorabilia sold at auction.

Material from the 1960s, seen by many as rock's golden years, is the most sought-after. Apart from The Beatles, the other most collectable artists include The Rolling Stones, The Jimi Hendrix Experience, Bob Dylan, The Doors and The Who. From the 1950s, Buddy Holly and Elvis Presley dominate the market. Contemporary artists such as Michael Jackson, Madonna and Prince are also well-represented, and some of their clothing in particular has commanded very high prices in recent years.

In general, memorabilia associated with the most important performers is the most sought-after and commands the highest prices. However, the length of a star's career is no guarantee as to collectability, and in some cases desirability seems to equate more with the impact and influence the artist has had in rock and pop's development. The Sex Pistols, for example, although together for only a couple of years, caused long-lasting shock waves that reverberated through the rock industry. Consequently, interest in, and prices paid for, Pistols' items has increased markedly, and the relative shortage of these should ensure their long-term desirability.

As is clear from these pages, rock and pop memorabilia is a colourful, highly diverse and exciting area. Buying for investment can prove to be a hazardous business in such a new and fast-developing market and, as in all other areas of collecting, the principle – buy it if you like it and can afford it – is a good one to follow. Happy hunting!

STEPHEN MAYCOCK

Signed Ephemera

Signed or manuscript items are probably the most popular rock and roll collectables. This is not only due to the amount of material available, but also because it is largely paper-based and can be easily stored. Signed ephemera is ideal for displaying, particularly if framed with a photograph of the artist. Values of Beatles-related material far exceed almost anything else, and demand for such items has been consistent.

It is the signatures of those stars who are no longer alive that tend to be the most sought-after – those of John Lennon, Jimi Hendrix, Jim Morrison, Brian Jones and Janis Joplin all command high prices. Death does not guarantee high prices for autographed material, but it does mean that the supply is finite unless an undiscovered collection is found somewhere.

The value of certain rock stars' autographs has increased so much that forgeries abound. The forger's task is made relatively easy because there is an abundance of inexpensive period material for them to use. In the case of The Beatles' signatures fakes are even more difficult to detect because during the 1960s non-genuine signatures were being produced in large numbers from a variety of sources. Towards the end of 1963 and in early 1964 when the Beatle-mania had taken a firm hold, requests for the band's autographs were overwhelming. In an attempt to try and keep pace with this demand it is known that as well as The Beatles, Brian Epstein, road managers Neil Aspinall and Mal Evans, Fan Club staff and even some members of the group's families all supplied sets of signatures. Although fakes, they were produced for no other reason than to keep fans happy, quite a different motivation from that behind modern forgers whose only intention is to make money. In the 1960s the only way to have been certain of obtaining genuine Beatles' signatures was to get close enough to the group to see each member of the band sign individually. It was common for fans to hand in autograph books or programmes at stage doors after concerts and to collect them in due course with the "signatures" in them.

Many were genuine, but it is a shock to discover that some long-treasured autographs are in fact fakes.

So how can one tell, years later, whether a set of signatures is genuine? Unfortunately there is no easy answer. There is no substitute for experience – for seeing as many examples as possible of all the variations in circulation. It is advisable to attend auctions and collectors' fairs, examine the material on view carefully, and compare against a genuine signature. Past auction catalogues are a valuable source of reference in this respect and are usually obtainable from the relevant auction house. Some autographs are accompanied by letters of authenticity, but these should be regarded with some suspicion, because although the time and place of the signing may indeed be historically correct these letters are more often than not a way of tricking innocent purchasers into buying fakes.

Any reputable auction house or dealer should provide a guarantee for the material they offer, stating that they will refund the purchase price of a lot which is shown to be a forgery if it is returned to them within a specified period. To prevent expensive mistakes, avoid buying a signed item if you have any doubts as to its authenticity and where there is no such guarantee.

Left: An album cover for Imagine, **Apple Records, 1971, signed and inscribed on the front and annotated with a caricature.**

Above: A cover of the album Planet Waves *signed by Bob Dylan and all the members of his band.*

Signed Pictures

Signed pictures fall into several categories: photographs taken out of magazines and books by the fan (the largest group); professional photographs not used for publicity purposes (see pp.122-123); and more rarely, amateur photographs taken by fans at concerts and other venues. The 1960s was a particularly rich period for photographs – The Beatles were featured in thousands of magazines and newspapers and fans would haunt the group's Abbey Road studios to get pictures signed. In general, the photograph itself is of no commercial value and collectors are paying for the signature against the image. Cuttings from 1960s' magazines which have recently been signed by the star are never as valuable as a picture with a period signature. They are easily recognizable because most signatures have changed over the years. Condition is not a major factor: being inxepensive at the time, pictures were often folded or stuck on walls with sticky tape and very few will be in pristine condition.

▲ ▼ These 1960s' pictures have been signed by members of The Beatles in more recent years. Both Paul McCartney and Ringo Starr appear regularly at concerts and it is not difficult to get things signed by them today. The Beatles' signatures are relatively easy to date; only Ringo's has stayed unchanged over the years. The thick felt tip pen immediately dates them to later than the 1960s when ball-point would have been used. **£100-300**

◀ Interest in The Beatles extends to every aspect of their life, even to when they were unknown schoolboys. This very rare school photograph shows Paul McCartney at the age of 14 (fourth from left, back row) at the Liverpool Institute High School in April 1956. It belonged to one of Paul's school friends who had it signed by 32 of his fellow pupils, including McCartney. Without his signature it would be worth only a quarter of the price.

£1,000

▼ Examples of Chuck Berry's signature are rare and most of those that do exist are recent additions to

1960s' photographs, as in the example above.

£80-120

▶ In this rare and personal photograph The Beatles are pictured with Mike Millward and his parents and girlfriend. Millward was a member of another group managed by Brian Epstein. The photograph was taken backstage, probably when the two bands appeared on the same bill in around 1963. In addition to the individual signatures, it has been personalized, and signed from "The Beatles" – any items bearing the name of the group are at a premium. Early items such as this were written in ink which is in danger of wearing off – ball point pen is far more preferable, and pencil signatures survive best of all.

£500+

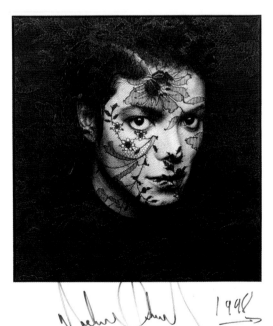

▲ This photograph of the Rolling Stones from 1964 is in good condition for its age and the yellow tape marks will not affect the value as they can be hidden by a frame. Although impossible to know exactly when it was signed, it cannot be after 1969 as Brian Jones died in that year. There is an odd disparity between prices paid for Beatles' signed material and that of The Stones, which is worth less than half as much.

£300

◀ This signed professional photograph of Michael Jackson in the 1980s is particularly desirable because the image has never been published. More recent stars tend to command lower prices, but Michael Jackson is an exception. The quirky wrong 1998 date is a typical addition to Jackson's signature. Unusually, this photograph would be collectable even without the signature because of the quality of the image.

£400+

▶ Signatures on individual pages from an autograph book can look fairly untidy on their own and are difficult to display, so it is not uncommon to find autographs attractively mounted and framed with a good image of the star. This example of Jim Morrison's signature is particularly collectable as it is inscribed "to the L.A. Woman", the title of The Doors' album released just before Morrison's death in 1971. It also bears a personal inscription. If the picture had simply been signed it would be worth only half the value.

£1,000+

▶ This attractive machine-printed photograph of Bob Marley is one of the few items signed by him. Since his death in 1981 there has been renewed interest in his music and contribution to the reggae movement, and any items associated with him are now highly sought-after.

£220-250

Farewell from the Cream

◀ Posters of a group or artist are frequently inserted inside album sleeves for fans to stick on their walls. Without a signature they have a nominal value, but occasionally signed examples appear on the market. This poster came with Cream's album *Goodbye* (1969) and has been signed recently by the three ex-members of the band in "sharpy" (silver pen) and black pen. The album was issued after the group had broken up (in 1968) and the poster is likely to have been signed by the members of the band on different occasions. This poster was inserted in the sleeve of a recent pressing and the signatures are modern, but because anything signed by the group is particularly rare this item is still very collectable. The large image (23 x 22in, 58 x 22cm) makes a good display item.

£380-420

Concert Programmes

Concert programmes are an attractive souvenir of a concert visit and are ideal items to have signed. It is always better to have precise details such as a date and location attached to a signature, as this gives the piece a historical context (signatures in an autograph book have little historical or autobiographical significance). Concert programmes in good condition generally fetch more than folded, creased or torn ones, even if they are for exactly the same concert and bear the same signatures. Usually, concert programmes from the 1950s and 1960s are particularly collectable.

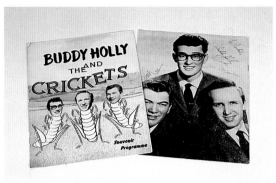

▲ Buddy Holly and The Crickets performed mainly in the United States and few concert programmes appear for sale outside of the country. This rare programme is for their only tour to the United Kingdom, in March 1958.

£800-1,000

▼ This rare programme for The Beatles' 1963 three-day tour of Scotland is specifically dated because the same programme design was often used at a number of venues over several months. Ringo Starr's signature is missing which lowers the value, but this is not as significant as it would be if John Lennon's signature were missing. Lennon is the most collectable Beatle and his signature is of course no longer available.
*There is evidence of brown tape having been used on the corners of this programme where it has been stuck on a wall, but in this case it will not have any effect on the value because the signatures are clear and the image of The Beatles is a good one.

£600

▼ This concert programme is from The Rolling Stones' January 1964 tour, when they were supporting The Ronettes, who had several hit records in the 1960s. The signatures are gocd and clear and because the programme is from so early on in the Stones' career it is particularly desirable. Few signed examples of this programme have appeared so far.

£400-500

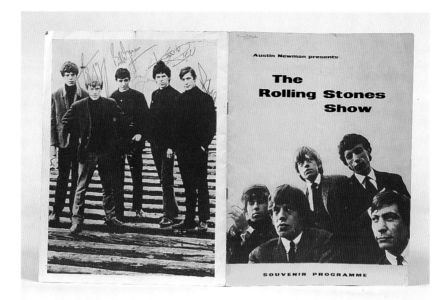

▲ The Rolling Stones, no longer a support band in 1964, feature prominently on the front of this programme as well as the back. Supply of their signatures has grown significantly and such signed programmes are less valuable than earlier ones.

£300-400

▼ Concert programmes for The Beatles rarely appear on the market outside the country in which they performed and any that do are particularly desirable. This example, for their tour of Australia in 1964, was sold in London in 1992.

£800-1,000

◀ Eric Clapton has enjoyed a revival in popularity in the late 1980s and early 1990s. He has returned to touring and his signature from the last few years is common. Examples from the 1960s are much more sought-after and harder to find, especially those examples from his time with the Yardbirds and Cream. This signed programme from the 1970s is much more affordable than earlier examples, but it is likely to rise in value.

£40-60

▲▲ This "Playing Cards" programme for The Beatles' 1964 UK tour is particularly interesting as the inside is signed by roadie Neil Aspinall, who signed many items for the band. He has signed himself "Paul McCartney alias Neil Aspinall". The closeness to McCartney's signature is evident if you compare it to the front of the programme. This item is invaluable as a reference for authentication, and is the only known example to have been sold.

£1,200+

◀ This programme is for a UK tour the Jimi Hendrix Experience undertook in April 1967 with the bizarre line-up of Cat Stevens, the Walker Brothers and Engelbert Humperdinck. It has been signed by Jimi Hendrix and Mitch Mitchell, but lacks bassist Noel Redding's signature. Although Hendrix signed many items, a sudden increase in demand has led to prices almost doubling recently.

£400-600

▼ Signed by Phil Lynott, Snowy White, Scott Gorham and Brian Downey, this programme from Thin Lizzy's 1981 *Renegade* tour is an attractive display item. Formed in Ireland in 1969 by Lynott, Downey and Eric Bell, the band began to enjoy commercial success following a move to London in 1970. The band's line up changed regularly – one of

the better-known members was Gary Moore (ex-Skid Row). Thin Lizzy peaked commercially in the late 1970s with the albums *Bad Reputation* (1977), *Live And Dangerous* (1978) and *Black Rose* (1979). The album *Renegade*, released in 1981 was less successful; Lynott had begun a parallel solo career in 1980 and in 1983 the band finally broke up. Lynott continued with his solo career, and reached the top five in 1985 playing on Gary Moore's single *Out In The Fields*. He died from a drug overdose in January 1986.

£100-150

▶ This signed itinerary is for Bill Haley's 1979 UK tour. However, the image on the front cover is from an earlier date. Bill Haley was at the peak of his career as a rock star for only a short period between 1953 and 1955, and throughout the 1960s and 1970s he was to a large extent playing only old material. Vintage 1950s signatures are therefore the most desirable (and the rarest), but this itinerary is still interesting to the collector because it is unusual, and so far seems to be the only signed example.

£200-300

Books and Magazines

Most signed books which come on the market are by John Lennon. His first book *In His Own Write* (1964) was a collection of his illustrated stories, together with nonsense verse and bizarre cartoons. This was followed by a similar collection, *Spaniard In The Works* (1965), and a compendium of the two books, *The Penguin John Lennon* (1966). Signed examples are not rare as Lennon attended official signing sessions and lunches. First editions in good condition are the most desirable.

Magazines signed on a relevant page by a rock star (usually over their image) are quite rare as most fans simply tore out the signed page and discarded the rest (see pp. 12-15). Complete dated editions are more interesting to the collector than single pages as they provide a tangible historical record. Although condition is important, if the magazine is rare it will still be valuable even if slightly worn.

▼ One of the most valuable signed Beatles' items is this biographical booklet issued by Apple in 1971. It has been annotated by John Lennon, whose personal comments appear on nearly every page, on matters related to members of the group and events in their careers. He has also added information about his relationship with Yoko Ono. The uniqueness of the piece is reflected in the price.

£20,000+

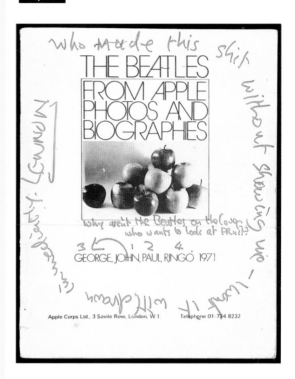

◀ Although Andy Warhol was not a musician he had strong associations with the rock and pop world through his famous "pop art" portraits of such artists as Mick Jagger, and through his involvement with the band The Velvet Underground. This copy of Andy Warhol's philosophy book would be of minimal value on its own, but the addition of Warhol's signature and his trademark drawing of the Campbell's soup tin make it a very desirable item.

£350-400

▼ This book was produced as a record of the Live Aid charity concert held at Wembley in July 1985. Although it has been signed by many of the artists who appeared at the concert it is in poor condition and the signatures are not very clear as many were written over colour pictures. A signed Live Aid poster auctioned to raise money for the charity is worth significantly more (see p. 28). **£170**

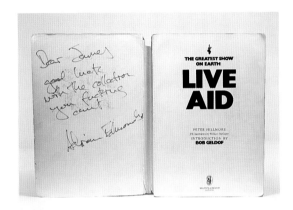

▲ This signed page from *Pop Weekly* is particularly interesting to Beatles' fans as it is from the 5 October 1962 edition, the date the group's first single *Love Me Do* was released by Parlophone Records. The value is increased by the fact that the page is in very good condition (it is not the cover and has not been exposed to sunlight), it is a complete edition, and the signatures are strong and clear. Significantly for earlier signed Beatles' material, the group has taken obvious care in signing the advertisement, using the white spaces when possible.

£500-700

◄ Signed examples of *The Penguin John Lennon* (released in paperback) are extremely rare, probably because at this time The Beatles had stopped touring the country and were far less accessible to the public than in their earlier years. This example was signed in 1966 during the filming of Lennon's *How I Won The War*. It is made more desirable by the addition of the personalized inscription to "Phylis the type" (a continuity girl on the film) and the humorous Lennon caricature, which is collectable and valuable in its own right. **£400**

◄ In 1964 Yoko Ono published *Grapefruit*, a collection of contemporary sayings and writings, but as she was virtually unknown, the first editions were not signed. It is only the second edition, published in 1970 after her marriage to John Lennon, that were. The couple were totally inseparable at this time and sat side by side at signing sessions. The addition of John Lennon's signature increases the value considerably. **£220-280**

Record Sleeves

Record sleeves, like concert programmes, are popular items to have signed. It is much more common to find the record sleeve signed than the record label which is usually dark in colour and difficult to write on. The presence of or even lack of a record does not affect the price as sleeve designs remain unchanged, but it is important that the sleeves are in good condition. Generally, the most successful titles command the higher prices, as do those in short supply. In addition to any sleeves signed by The Beatles, those signed by The Rolling Stones in the early 1960s are popular and highly collectable.

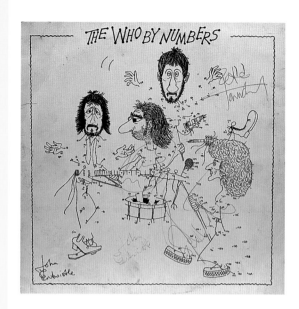

▲ *The Who By Numbers* album was released in 1975 with a cover that featured cartoons by John Entwistle (see p. 49). Signed examples of The Who material are rare and even though this sleeve is rather dirty and discoloured it is still desirable. **£150**

◄ Record sleeves bearing Buddy Holly's signature and those of the Crickets are highly sought-after. Examples tend to be "contrived", as with this reissue of the Crickets' first album which has been signed recently by three of the band's members. The problem of Buddy Holly's missing name has been resolved by framing the cover with a page from an autograph book bearing a 1950's example of his signature. **£500-600**

▲ Material signed by Elvis Presley is surprisingly inexpensive considering he was one of the giants of rock and roll. This signed example of *Speedway*, released in 1968, is in superb condition and is carefully signed but the price is quite low. **£200**

▼ Every Christmas between 1963 and 1969 the Beatles' Fan Club produced a special 45rpm flexi-disc for its members with jokey messages from the band. These are not rare, but those that are signed and in mint condition or still in the envelope they were mailed in are very collectable. If this 1967 disc were signed by all The Beatles it would be worth more. **£300-350**

▼ The Rolling Stones' EP *Five By Five* (so-called because it contains five tracks by the five members of The Rolling Stones) was released in 1964. This particular example shows distinct signs of age and has brown tape marks around the edge. However, the signatures of The Rolling Stones are very good examples and are surprisingly clear considering the surface would have been difficult to write on. Because this is an particularly good signed example, the value is suitably high.

£300-400

▼ The Beatles' first single release *Love Me Do/PS I Love You* (1962) was one of only two discs with a red label, which could be signed (after this Parlophone used black). The Beatles held a signing session, so quite a few signed examples exist. Prices depends on the quality of the signatures and on which side the record has been signed.

£600-1,000

▼ This example of *The Velvet Underground And Nico* is a very desirable piece beause it is a first issue (released by the group in 1967). These first records had a peel-off banana on the sleeve but very few have remained in the un-peeled condition of this one. The value is further increased by the sleeve's excellent condition and the addition of the signature of Andy Warhol, who introduced Nico to the band and produced the album. The fact that it was probably signed later will not greatly affect the value.

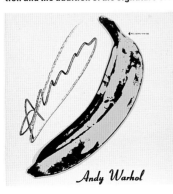

£400

◀ The death of Freddie Mercury in 1991 has led the value of Queen material to rise notably in recent years; and there has been an increase in the number of items appearing for sale. *A Night At The Opera*, released in 1975, features the band's best-known single *Bohemian Rhapsody*. In good condition it is worth around £260 whereas before Mercury's death it would have only been worth around £50. Queen material will become more rare in years to come as demand increases.

£160-180

▼ In the past Bob Dylan has been rather reclusive and examples of his signature from the 1960s and 1970s are extremely scarce and therefore very desirable. Although this album is from 1992 it is in good condition

and it has a clear and good example of a signature which is notoriously hard to come by.

£300+

▼ ▶ Marc Bolan has a small but dedicated following among rock and roll collectors. There is no shortage of material associated with him – articles of clothing appear for sale quite regularly (see pp. 84-5) – and items signed by him are relatively inexpensive. However, this signed sleeve of T. Rex's album

Futuristic Dragon is particularly collectable because it is accompanied by a note written by Marc Bolan to a fan he was unable to meet. The letter has quirky personal touches which give the piece added appeal, including spelling errors (ie "glasgo flu"); and it has been written on hotel headed paper which places it within a historical context. Both items would be collectable in their own right, but are more desirable as a pair. This particular record was a factory sample which also adds to the value.

£180-250

BEWARE

Although these are genuine 1960's album sleeves The Beatles' signatures are fakes. The Beatles would never have signed their names in the purple felt tip pen used on the top example shown here; they usually signed in black or blue biro at this time. Fakes are not always obvious and it is only years of experience that can teach the expert to recognize them. However, one of the best ways of identifying fakes is to compare them with a known set of original signatures (see p. 18).

▼ This novelty picture disc single of *Brown Sugar* in the shape of the Rolling Stones' famous tongue logo has been signed on the transparent sleeve by Mick Jagger and is a fun item for Stones' fans to collect. However, the value would be significantly greater if it had been signed by each member of the band – in good condition it would fetch at least £200.

£60-80

▲ Elton John was one of the most successful artists of the 1970s and *Goodbye Yellow Brick Road* (1973) was one of his most notable albums. The double album was released at a time when Elton John was establishing his career as a rock and roll artist and it is a particularly good example to have signed by him. Record sleeves signed by Elton John rarely appear on the market so prices for those in good condition tend to be relatively high. Other items associated with Elton John are far more abundant, particularly after the sale of many of his possessions at a London auction house in 1988.

£100-150

Publicity Material

Most of the signed publicity material on the market today is in the form of publicity cards. These were given out in vast quantities as part of the general promotional activities of record companies, often for the release of a new album. In the 1960s they were standard postcard-sized black and white publicity photographs, but in recent years there has been a greater variety of size and some have been produced in colour. The cards themselves are not at all valuable but with the addition of a collectable signature such as that of one of The Beatles, they can become so. The most highly sought-after publicity cards and posters are those signed by the most successful artists; and any cards which are slightly more unusual will also fetch higher prices. Condition is important and the signature should be legible – only very rare examples are collectable in poor condition. A few publicity posters were signed and when these are offered for sale they tend to be expensive.

▲ This 1957 publicity card for Buddy Holly and The Crickets is extremely rare. It is signed with only Christian names which suggests it was for someone the band knew. The reverse is addressed in Buddy Holly's hand and postmarked Dec. 31 1957 from Texas.

£600-800

▼ The signed reverse sides of these two Parlophone Beatles' publicity cards demonstrate an interesting progression in the style of the group's signatures. The card on the left dates from the beginning of the group's career in late 1962 (Ringo Starr joined in August 1962) and the signatures are quite simple and restrained. The card on the right is from early 1963 when the group had signed far more material and their signatures are more sophisticated. The fact that the cards are not in very good condition (there are yellow tape marks) will not affect the value.

£600-700

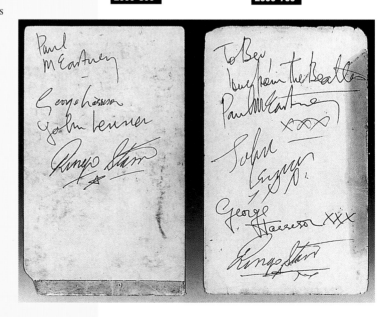

▼ The fact that this was the only colour publicity card for The Beatles immediately makes it highly collectable. In addition, it has been personally addressed to Don Andrew, a member of Remo 4, a fellow Liverpool band who toured with The Beatles in 1964. Paul has signed himself "Fatty" and John "Bonnie", which adds a personal touch. Many different publicity cards were produced for The Beatles and keen collectors may try and obtain a signed copy of each variety for their collection.

£900+

▲ Even relatively recent promotional material can fetch high prices: this framed poster for Madonna's *Blond Ambition World Tour 90* at the Los Angeles Sports Arena, is signed in silver pen by artist Michael Dole, and in black ballpoint by Madonna herself. The signatures make the piece particularly collectable.

£300-350

FAKES

There is no shortage of 1960s' material today, which makes the job of identifying fakes that much more difficult. This publicity card is a good example of a fake Beatles' signature. The signatures have been signed in black on dark areas, deliberately creating "poor contrast" so that you cannot see them properly. At this time The Beatles would have signed in all the white areas available. Another way to check signatures is to compare with a known original (see p.18).

◄ This is the earliest publicity shot of The Rolling Stones and shows the band with short hair cuts. It is a typical 1960s' small black and white publicity card and has been signed in red, blue and green ball-point which make it more colourful. The care The Stones have taken to ensure their signatures are visible reflects their newness to stardom. The card's excellent condition and the fact it is a very early example add to its value – cards from 1964 onwards are far more abundant.

£400

▼ A charity event similar to Live Aid was held in the United States in 1985, entitled USA for Africa. This is one of 40 posters for the event, signed by the stars who appeared on the single, *We Are The World*, and sold at various functions to raise money for charity. Although not as colourful as the Live Aid poster, the signatures are far more prominent .

£800-1,200

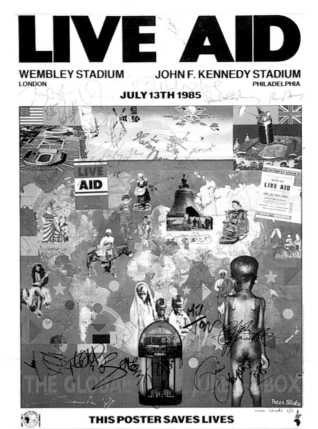

◀ The artist Peter Blake, who designed the cover for The Beatles' *Sergeant Pepper* album, was specially commissioned to design a poster for the Live Aid concert held in Britain on 13 July 1985 to raise money for the starving in Africa. This is one of only two examples signed by Blake and all the artists at the concert. The attractive design will appeal both as an image and a signed piece of rock memorabilia.

£4,000-5,000

▶ Jimi Hendrix's inscription and signature have faded so badly on this poster that they are barely visible in this photograph. The poster was signed by Hendrix at York University on 18 February 1967 whilst he was on a tour. The inscription, "Stay as sweet and cute as you are. Hope to see you again Love", is a typical Hendrix message to a girl fan; characteristic messages found on items addressed to male fans include "Stay cool" and "Stay groovy". Although the poster is in fairly poor condition (it is yellowing and torn) and the inscription is very faint, it is still very valuable as it is rare to find such a large signed Hendrix item (16½ x 20in, 41 x 50cm). Interest in Jimi Hendrix has rocketed since his guitar sold at auction in 1990 for £198,000 (see p. 99) sparking off a collecting passion for Hendrix material which has spread to all areas, including his lyrics and clothing. A standard Hendrix signature worth around £200 before the 1990 sale would now be worth twice that amount.   **£900**

▼ This is typical of the numerous 8in x 10in (20 x 25.5cm) Madonna publicity photographs which have been produced in both black and white and colour in recent years. The inscription, "Strike a pose", taken from Madonna's *Vogue* album, adds character and will increase the value. Madonna has suddenly become very collectable; and anything associated with her that is more unusual is particularly desirable.

£350-400

▼ This portion of a concert hand-bill signed on the reverse by five of the seven members of the band Lynyrd Skynyrd is interesting as very little material relating to

the band comes on the market. The band's singer, Ronnie van Zant, was killed and several of the other members were injured in a plane crash when the plane fell in the Mississippi Swamps at the start of the band's US tour in October 1977.

£50-70

▲ Because The Sex Pistols were together for such a short time any material signed by the band is rare. This publicity card has been clearly signed by each member of The Sex Pistols and has then been mounted for display purposes with a copy of their single, *Anarchy In The UK*, and a photocopy of an original handbill. Although these extra items sold with the publicity card provide some interesting historical information they do not add to the value of the band's signatures which are highly collectable in their own right.

£400+

Playlists

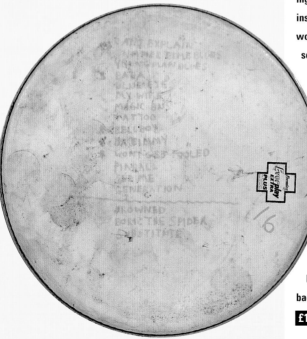

Because playlists tend not to survive after a concert they are rare and can be very valuable. They provide an informative souvenir because they contain a list, usually written in the hand of the artist, of song titles in the order they would have been sung at a particular concert, and may be the only record of what was actually played. Most playlists are on scraps of paper on which the artist would have hastily written the titles before going on stage; others may have been written out carefully beforehand; and very rarely the lists would be written on drum skins. In some cases each member of a band would have been given his or her own copy.

The Beatles at The Oasis Club.

1. The Hippy Hippy Shake
2. Sweet Little Sixteen
3. The Sheik of Araby
4. September In the Rain
5. Dizzy Miss Lizzie
6. Take Good Care of My Baby
7. 'Til There Was You
8. Memphis Tennesse
9. What A Crazy World We Live In
10. Like Dreamers Do
11. Money
12. Young Blood
13. Honeymoon Song
14. Hullo Little Girl
15. So How 'Come (Everly's)
16. Oo My Soul
17. To Know Her is to Love Her or Hully Gully
18. Roll Over Beethoven
19. The Love of the Loved
20. Dance/Twist In the Streets
21. Dream
22. Searchin.

▼ **The Who are one of a few bands known to have written their playlists on drum skins. Because Keith Moon had a habit of putting his drinks down on his drums his roadies devised a method of writing the list in reverse on the inside of the skin so the titles would not be wiped out – some letters are obviously back-to-front in this example. This list from the mid-1970s provides a permanent record of the band's famous songs and is therefore highly desirable. An asterisk indicates those songs for which Keith Moon had to wear headphones to hear the backing-track.**

£1,800+

▲ **This is an exceptionally early set list for The Beatles before they were famous, for when they made only their second appearance outside Merseyside under Brian Epstein's management, at the Oasis Club in Manchester in February 1962. The songs are typed, which indicates the degree of forethought given to the band's early performances. The list was sold by The Beatles' early drummer, Pete Best, who would have had it taped to his drum kit. It lists 22 song titles, many unrecorded, and is a valuable record of the band's vast repertoire (they were singing over one hundred songs at this time). If the list were hand-written, it would be worth far more.**

£800+

▶ Anything in John Lennon's handwriting is highly desirable. This playlist from 1963 shows a list of ten abbreviated song titles, most of which are very famous hits today. The machine-print of Lennon, although attractive, will not add to the value of this already highly important collector's item.

£2,000

▲ A rare piece, this playlist for a concert featuring eleven abbreviated song titles, was written by John Lennon. There is a signed dedication on the back. Although it is undated, the song titles suggest that the list was written slightly later than the one above – some time between January and April 1964.

£2,000+

▶ Manuscripts which record particularly interesting events always command a premium. This set list was written by Jimi Hendrix for his monumental concert at Woodstock in 1969 which was recorded on film, establishing him as one of the greatest performers in music history. It is interesting that for such an important event Hendrix casually wrote the titles of the songs he was going to perform on a piece of paper torn from a notebook – it is evident from his crossings out that he changed the order as he went along.

£2,000-3,000

◀ Even though this early Queen set list is not the original, but only a carbon copy (each member of the band would have been given one), it is still sought-after because it is so rare. It was produced for Queen's concert at the King's College Hospital on 10 March 1972 and provides an early record of the songs the band were playing before they became famous.

£100

Beatles' Lyrics

Because lyrics are among the most expensive types of rock and roll memorabilia and because The Beatles are the most collectable band, any lyrics written by either Paul McCartney or John Lennon are exceptionally desirable, and many have set new world records for rock and pop memorabilia when sold at auction. Lyrics written by Lennon tend to fetch slightly more than songs by McCartney. As with lyrics generally, the most popular and the rarest titles are the most valuable. A large number of Beatles' lyrics have come on the market through the band's road manager, the late Mal Evans. John Lennon wrote most of his songs on any paper to hand, and it is likely that many were only written down once. Signed replicas and final recording copies of songs do appear, but these are far less valuable than originals. Songs written by Lennon and McCartney as solo artists fetch lower prices – several handwritten versions have sold in recent years for around £6,000.

▼ An unusual piece, this postcard contains lyrics for an unpublished song by John Lennon in 1966. The card itself was sent by Japanese fans to George Harrison, and his name and address appear on the front, together with a list of rhyming words written by Lennon as he was composing: *dream/deam/ beam/scene/stream*.

£3,000-4,000

▲ The price difference between the lyrics of Lennon and McCartney for The Beatles and other members is evident in the price realised for these handwritten lyrics by George Harrison for *While My Guitar Gently Weeps*, Although a prolific writer, few of his songs are as famous as this one.

£6,000-8,000

◀ These lyrics for *Heavenly* were written down by Stuart Sutcliffe in around 1960. They appear in blue ink on a piece of lined paper torn from a notebook, and measure 6½ x 5in (16.5 x 12.7cm). An early draft, they feature some deletions and alterations. The subject of a recent film *Backbeat*, bassist Sutcliffe left The Beatles in 1961 to live in Hamburg with his girlfriend, photographer Astrid Kirchherr, and concentrate on his painting (see p.45 and p.124). Sutcliffe died in April 1962.

£300-500

*I read the news today, oh boy
about a lucky man who made the grade
and though the news was rather sad
well I just had to laugh
I saw the photograph
He blew his mind out in a car
he didn't notice that the lights had changed
a crowd of people stood and stared
they'd seen his face before
nobody was really sure if he was from the House of Lords.
I saw a film today oh boy
the English army had just won the war
a crowd of people turned away
well I just had to look
having read the book.
I read the news today oh boy
4000 holes in Blackburn Lancashire
and though the holes were rather small
they had to count them all
now they know how many holes it takes to fill
the Albert Hall*

◀ These handwritten lyrics by John Lennon for *A Day In The Life* (1967) broke the world record when they sold at auction in 1992. The lyrics are particularly collectable because they are regarded by many as the words to his most important song, which appeared on the group's most famous album, *Sergeant Pepper*. This side of the paper shows the working copy of the lyrics – on the reverse is a neat version. There are slight differences in the recorded version, and the middle section (written by Paul McCartney) is missing here. In the same auction, Paul's lyrics for *She's Leaving Home* made a total of £45,100.

£45,000-50,000

▲ Not all The Beatles' lyrics fetch record prices. These handwritten working lyrics by John Lennon for *Because* show only five lines, which may account for the relatively low estimate. They have been written on the back of a business letter to The Beatles by John East-man in July 1969, and this not only demon-strates the spontaneity of John's songs (composed on the spot), but also tracks down the cre-ative moment to a specific time and place. The song was recorded a month later at the Abbey Road Studios.

£7,000-8,000

▼ These Lennon lyrics for *I Am The Walrus* (1967) show several variations from the final version (including the line "boy you've been a lucky girl, you let your knickers down", which was changed to "boy you've been a naughty girl ..."). They sold for £44,000 in 1993, but no doubt would have fetched even more if complete.

▲ These John Lennon lyrics for *You've Got To Hide Your Love Away* (1965) were sold by Lennon's chauffeur. He was driving Lennon to the studios when he was asked for something to write on: this address book was the only thing available, and Lennon proceeded to write down the words of the song, again showing the spontaneity of much of The Beatles' songwriting.

£25,000-30,000

Lyrics

Apart from a guitar used on a classic recording or a costume worn on a special tour, handwritten lyrics are one of the most personal things associated with an artist, reflecting the thought process of the artist as he or she is composing a song. They often have crossings out and alterations and many show subtle differences from the final recorded version. Most are written on the spur of the moment on whatever paper is to hand, and this gives them an immediacy not found on records. Few contemporary lyrics come on the market, and this possibly reflects the trend towards using word processors. The most collectable lyrics are those for the most famous or successful song recorded by an artist. However, the lyrics for an obscure song by a famous artist which has never been recorded will be highly sought-after. Lyrics are quite rare and tend to come into circulation by accident – many are thrown away after a recording session and retrieved by chance from waste paper baskets. Because of this condition is not crucial and coffee stains, for example, add authenticity rather than detract from their value.

▼ Very few of Buddy Holly's best-known lyrics come on the market, but a number were sold by his family in New York. These Buddy Holly lyrics from the late 1950s are particularly interesting because they are for a song that was never recorded. Written in ballpoint pen and pencil, the corrections show the thought process of a highly important artist at work.

£750-850

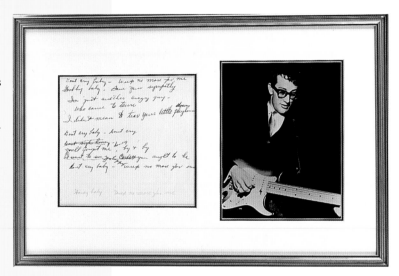

▼ Bruce Springsteen is one of the most popular and successful artists of the last 15 years, and along with Jimi Hendrix and Jim Morrison, his lyrics appear quite regularly on the market, particularly in recent years. These lyrics are an early draft for *Meeting Across The River* released on Springsteen's *Born To Run* album in 1975 which launched him into stardom. The many deletions and extensive revisions in ink and pencil are particularly interesting.

£1,000-1,500

▲ ▶ Jimi Hendrix was a prodigious writer and several examples of his lyrics have appeared on the market. These lyrics are exceptional because they combine so many interesting elements, and the fact that the sheet is quite scruffy and has parts missing is unimportant. Not only are the lines for one of Hendrix's best-known songs – *Love Or Confusion* – they are accompanied by a detailed and amusing cartoon by Hendrix . The fact that the lyrics are written on headed paper from the Hyde Park Towers hotel, which gives a time and place to the writing of the song, adds further interest. Hendrix was frequently on tour and on the road and many of his lyrics were written on hotel or airline paper.

£6,000-8,000

▲ Most of Bob Dylan's lyrics are typed and then heavily annotated in ink or pencil. This working manuscript from c.1966 is for *Most Likely You Go Your Way And I'll Go Mine*, from the *Blonde On Blonde* album. Although a highly influential artist, his lyrics are probably worth only around a tenth of the value of those by John Lennon (see pp. 32-33).

£4,000

▼ Jim Morrison saw himself as a poet as well as a songwriter and published some poetry shortly before his death. These working lyrics are for *The Celebration Of The Lizard*, a stage performance that featured songs, poetry and music. The collection includes typewritten verses, annotated in blue ink, and seven handwritten verses of *Celebration* which show variations from the version printed on the inside cover of The Doors' third album *Waiting For The Sun*, 1968. **£4,000-5,000**

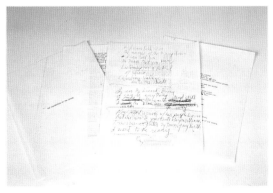

◀ Although not strictly lyrics, this score for *Waltz #1* written in c.1958 by Frank Zappa is an extremely interesting piece. Zappa who died earlier this year, was a highly innovative and talented musician, but recognized that his music was not to everyone's taste. A letter written by Zappa enclosed with this item reads "most of my output seldom falls into the "pretty category"". Born in Baltimore, Maryland in 1940, Zappa joined the Soul Giants in 1964 with Elliot Ingber, Roy Estrada, Jimmy Carl Black and Ray Collins. The band was later renamed the Mothers (changed to the Mothers of Invention by MGM). A prolific writer and experimentalist, Zappa was also a master of production technology. Regarded by some as a great composer, his album of electronic rock *The Perfect Stranger And Other Works* (1985) reached the top ten of the American classical music chart.

£250

▶ These lyrics are for *Wuthering Heights* which appeared on Kate Bush's first album *The Kick Inside* which she brought out in 1978. The song went to number one in the British charts in February of that year and established her as one of the few great British female vocalists of the period. The lyrics were sold, together with seven reel-to-reel tapes, as part of a set with nine other A4 sheets of lyrics, all of which have been neatly written out by Kate Bush in black felt-tip and blue ball-point pen .

The neatness of the lyrics makes them less interesting than if it were a working copy and suggests that they were written either for a recording session, or for reproduction on an album sleeve. However, because they are the only handwritten example of Kate Bush's lyrics to have appeared on the market and are in such a comprehensive form they will command a premium with the selected following Kate Bush has among fans today.

£2,500 for the set

▼ The Sex Pistols are the embodiment of punk rock and because the group were around for such a short time (1976-1977) any items associated with them are highly collectable. These handwritten lyrics by Johnny Rotten are for *Problems* which appeared on *Never Mind The Bollocks Here's The Sex Pistols* (1977), the only album released while the group were together. They are on Glitterbest headed paper – Malcolm McLaren's company – and the simplicity of the logo reflects the anti-establishment attitude of The Pistols. The neat writing suggests the lyrics were written out for the recording studio. The final words at the bottom of the page add a personal touch which will appeal to the collector.

£800-1,000

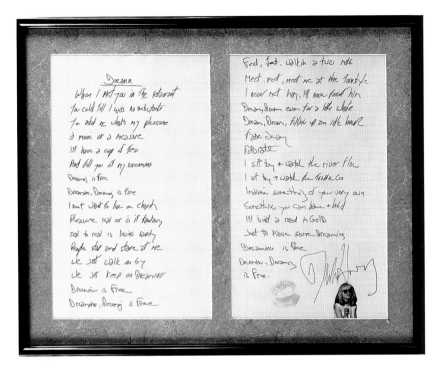

▲ Handwritten lyrics are rarely signed because they were intended for personal use. However, these Blondie lyrics for *Dreaming* (which reached number two in the British charts in 1979) were probably written out specially for donation to charity and they have the double signature of Debbie Harry's name and her lip imprint. Because this is a "contrived" piece, the value lies in the handwriting – as there is no display of the writer's thought process.

£400-700

▼ Marc Bolan was a prolific songwriter and because a number of his lyrics have appeared on the market in recent years they command relatively low prices. These lyrics for *Carsmile Song* written in around 1974 not only provide a good example of Bolan's idiosyncratic handwriting, but are also representative of his poetic style of composing. Provenance is provided by the fact that they were in the collection of Steve Little – a roadie for Marc Bolan's band T. Rex – for three and a half years.

The fact that half of the verses are typed suggests that the additional hand-written ones were the result of a subsequent train of thought.

£100-200

Contracts

There are two types of contract that come up for sale: those made between artist and promoter for appearances in concerts; and those for other business arrangements such as signing a band to a label, royalties or publishing agreements. Concert contracts are more desirable than business contracts, which are less common and not as informative. Usually the contracts are signed by the manager of the group and seldom bear the signature of the stars, but those from a group's early days before they had a manager may be signed by the artists themselves and are highly sought-after; some have no signature at all. Thus, unlike other signed material, in the case of contracts the collector is not paying for the signature, but for the historical document. Condition is very important as the contract is a written document and if any of the words are missing or illegible value will fall considerably. They are sought after by rock and pop collectors because they are a point of historical reference and may help to fill in gaps in a particular group's history. They are quite limited in supply, so prices tend to be high.

▼ This contract from 31 May 1965 is for the Yardbird's appearance on the BBC television programme *Pop Inn*. It is particularly collectable because it has been signed by the group's manager, George Gromelsky, who had previously been a very early manger of The Rolling Stones. Although perhaps not one of the most famous bands in history, the Yardbirds have a cult following with rock and roll collectors because among their members were three of the greatest rock guitarists of all time – Eric Clapton, Jimmy Page and Jeff Beck.

£180-200

▲ Jimi Hendrix's signature on this publishing contract from 12 May 1967 adds value to what is already a highly collectable historical document. It lists many of Hendrix's songs and also shows the very modest performance fee he commanded at this time.

£1,200-1,500

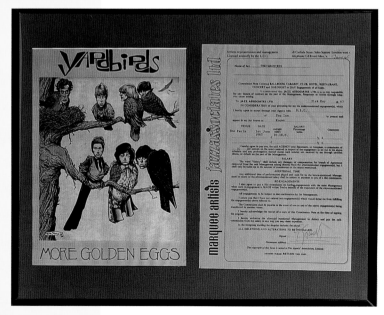

▼ This standard contract between Peacock Music Publishing Company and The Jacksons is attractive to the collector because it provides an example of all five of The Jacksons' signatures together.

£1,200-1,500

▼ This unsigned contract for The Rolling Stones' appearance at High Wycombe Town Hall on 13 August 1963 is fairly standard, but because it is an early Stones document with historical details it is still collectable. To make it more attractive, but adding little to value, it has been mounted with four ticket stubs and a letter to the band's manager.

£240-260

◄ This is an unsigned carbon copy of the original contract between The Beatles and their manager, Brian Epstein. It was signed by the band on 24 January 1962 at Epstein's NEMS office and a carbon copy was given to each member – no signed examples have come up at auction. Epstein did not sign it for some days and the band were without a legal contract for that period. It is very important as a historical document as it marks a leap in The Beatles' careers from a very successful local Liverpool band to national and global fame. **£4,000+**

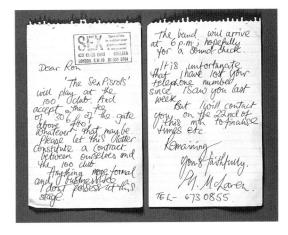

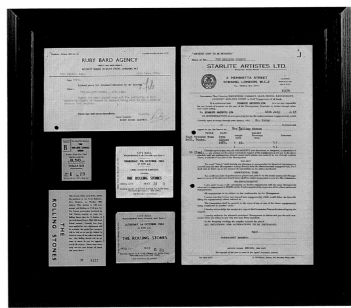

▲ Typical of the unconventional and rebellious image of punk rock and The Sex Pistols is this handwritten contract from Malcolm McLaren for The Sex Pistols to appear at the 100 Club in London in September 1976. It is on a piece of paper torn out from a notebook and the page has been casually stamped at the top with the name of McLaren's shop, *Sex*, which he ran with his dress designer partner Vivienne Westwood. Dating from the very beginning of the band's career in 1976, it is a good example of McLaren's casual approach to the music business.

£500-700+

Letters

Letters from rock and pop artists may relate to any-thing from personal affairs to business and fan letters, and in general the more intimate the letter is the greater its value. Most are hand written, but a few are typed and then signed by the artist. The letter is usually put on the market by the person to whom it was originally sent, although some change hands several times. John Lennon's ex-wife Cynthia has sold a number of her letters from him in recent years.

As with most printed ephemera, condition is important to value, particularly if parts of the text are missing. Handwritten letters are more desirable than typed ones, and any that still have their original envelopes will fetch more than ones without them.

Letters are usually bought for display and some have the added bonus of a drawing or cartoon which makes them more attractive. This is particularly true of letters by John Lennon who was an avid sketcher (see pp. 44-7). Letters written by The Beatles are the most desirable and several examples, particularly from the early years of their career, have appeared on the market in recent years.

◄▼ **This three-page letter was sent by Elvis Presley while in Germany with the army in October 1958, to Anita Wood, his girlfriend from 1957-1961. It is very intimate and reveals much about the young Elvis's character and a relationship not widely known about. It is rare to find such a personal letter by Elvis – most are brief ones written in the late 1950s and early 1960s.**

£4,500-5,000

▲ **This Jimi Hendrix letter is interesting because it refers to the much-publicised dissatisfaction of The Jimi Hendrix Experience with having been put on their first tour in 1967 with the rather bizarre line-up of Engelbert Humperdinck, the Walker Brothers and Cat Stevens. Written to a male fan in a chatty style, it includes an early example of Hendrix's highly-sought after signature, and is made more valuable because he has signed it with the name of the band.**

£2,500-3,000

▼ Because he is no longer alive, letters by Brian Jones fetch higher prices than those by other members of The Rolling Stones. Sent to a fan in July 1965, this short note does not reveal much; those which mention something specific about the band are more collectable.

▲ Although not dated, this letter was probably written by John Lennon in early 1963 (the group appeared at the Gaumont Cinema, Hanley on 3 March). Sent from his home in Liverpool where he lived with his Aunt Mimi, in it John advises an admirer about the band's fan club. The Beatles' increasing success throughout that year led to John replying to fewer and fewer fan letters due to a lack of time.

The letter still has its envelope which adds value.

£380-420

£1,000-1,500

▼ Letters which mention landmark events are highly desirable. This letter from George Harrison, written over September and October 1960 to his good friend Arthur Kelly, was sent from the Kaiserkeller Club in Hamburg, where The Beatles were on tour. In it he mentions the fellow Liverpool group, Rory Storm and The Hurricanes, and is uncomplimentary about them: "the only person who is any good in the group is the drummer …". This is Richard Starkey who two years later joined The Beatles as Ringo Starr. **£2,500-3,000**

◄ An important early letter from May 1962 written by George Harrison from the Star Club in Hamburg to a fan, these three pages contain the exciting news that the band has just been signed by EMI to the Parlophone label. Harrison's attitude is both optimistic and realistic: "We will just have to work hard & hope for a hit with whatever we record" – their first recording session was set for 6 June of that year. Harrison also mentions other artists appearing at the Star Club at that time, including Gerry and the Pacemakers, and the black singer, Davy Jones.

£1,500-2,000

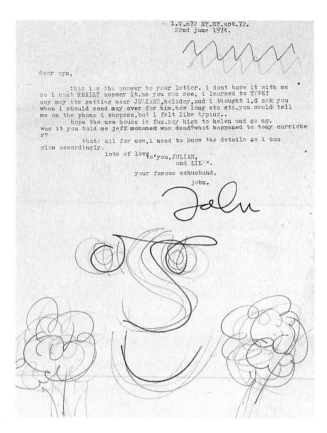

```
                               I.W.&72 NY.NY.apt.72.
                               22nd june 1974.

   dear cyn,

            this is the answer to your letter. i dont have it with me
   so i cant REALLY answer it.as you can see, i learned to TYPE!
   any way its getting near JULIANS,holiday,and i thought i,d ask you
   when i should send may over for him.how long etc etc.you could tell
   me on the phone i suppose,but i felt like typing..
            hope the new house is fun.say high to helen and ga ng.
   was it you told me jeff mohammed was dead?what happened to tony carricke
   r?
            thats all for now,i need to know the details so i can
   plan accordingly.
                              lots of love to'you,JULIAN,
                                        and LIL'*.
                      your famous exhusband,
                              john.
```

◀ **This is thought to be the only letter written by John Lennon to his ex-wife Cynthia after their divorce in 1968. It was one of several of Lennon's letters sold by Cynthia at auction. Although the text is typed, it still reflects John's humorous style. The value is increased significantly by the addition of the characteristic colourful cartoon which even on its own would be worth around £1,000.**

£2,500-3,000

▲ **This very short letter addressed to "Record Mirror Readers" was probably written for promotional purposes – the text is the title of the B side of *Let It Be*, The Beatles' last UK single released in March 1970. Although the text is not particularly interesting, it includes a good example of Lennon's signature and the characteristic John and Yoko cartoon logo used from around 1968/9.**

£1,500

▶ **This letter was written by Johnny Rotten to the editor of the fanzine *Youth Anthem* in early 1978, not long after the Sex Pistols broke up. It details many of Rotten's personal thoughts and explains why the group disbanded – "due mainly to Mr McLaren's paranoia and spite". It is rare to find such an open letter and Johnny Rotten's multi-signature on the bottom makes it even more desirable.**

£800-1,000

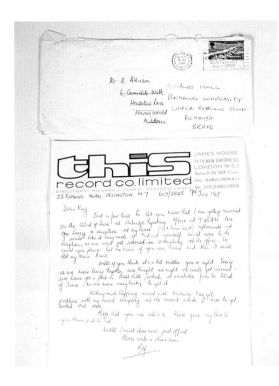

▲ Any early Elton John letters signed with his real name Reginald Dwight are vey rare. This one is inviting a friend to his wedding with Linda Woodrow, an event which never took place. Written when Elton was working as a session musician it highlights the struggles of an unknown singer. **£350-500**

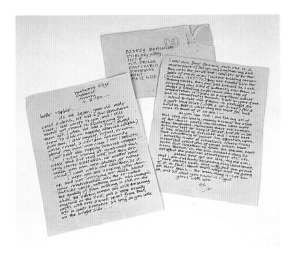

▼ Freddie Mercury wrote this letter to his former flatmate Celine on 26 October 1969, long before his fame with Queen. It gives good biographical information and is particularly desirable because of its early revelations about Mercury's sexuality. Also of interest is the comment that Led Zeppelin "were really great", as in just a few years Queen were to be as equally successful. Such an early and personal letter will always be at a premium, especially since Mercury's death in 1991. **£1,200-1,500**

◄ Much of Eric Clapton's character and personal thoughts are revealed in this letter to Raphie, a prisoner Clapton wrote to regularly as a pen friend. Not only does it show Clapton's opinion about the record trade, it also hints at his well-publicised problems with alcohol and drugs. It is in very good condition and the handwriting is neat and legible.

£250-300

Beatles' Drawings

John Lennon is one of a number of rock stars to have had a formal education in art. He attended the Liverpool College of Art with fellow Beatle, Stuart Sutcliffe. His work is by far the most likely to appear for sale at auction simply because he produced so much more than anyone else. He was an obsessive doodler, drawing on anything that came to hand, and examples of his work come in all shapes and sizes, from scribbles on scraps of paper to framed pieces of serious "art" (see also pp. 124-5). Most of his pencil drawings were done for himself and consequently very few are signed. He also published a large number of cartoons in several books (see pp.20-21) and the original artwork for these has come on the market in recent years. Many of his cartoons are variations on themes covered in these books – he had a particular interest in grotesques and deformities. Condition has a significant effect on value.

▲ John Lennon's distinctive style of drawing is clearly visible when comparing these two pictures, both drawn around 1964. The signature with a picture of a little man (top), appears in a copy of Lennon's book *In His*

Own Write (see p.20) that was given to Cynthia Lennon's brother. *In His Own Write* was published in 1964 by Jonathan Cape, London. This figure was one of those often used by Lennon when signing his name. After his marriage to Yoko Ono in 1969, Lennon usually drew cartoons of their faces to accompany their signatures, occasionally including their son Sean. The pen and ink drawing, *An Animated Group* (left), is a more formal example of one of his sketches.

£400-600 book

£1,500-2,000 drawing

◄◄ This very important hand-drawn Christmas card by John Lennon was given to his girlfriend Cynthia Powell in December 1958. Inside are eight pages of romantic verses which show his deep affection for her (Cynthia became his wife five years later, although their marriage ended in divorce). The card is in excellent condition and was a well-known and desirable piece even before it was sold in 1991; it had been featured in Ray Coleman's book, *John Winston Lennon, Volume I 1940-1966*, published by Sidgwick and Jackson in 1984.

£10,000

▼ ► The style of these Lennon cartoons is similar to that of his drawings for the book *In His Own Write* and they may have been ideas that weren't used. Like many sketches produced by Lennon they have been done on scraps of paper, suggesting their

► Among the more afford-able drawings are these figure studies drawn in c.1959 by

spontaneity. Provenance for items which have not been signed is very important to value. These drawings are definitely by Lennon as they were sold by his housekeeper Dot Jarlett to whom they were given.

Stuart Sutcliffe, John Lennon's best friend at Liverpool College, and a very big influence on his art. He was persuaded to join The Beatles by Lennon in 1960 as a bass player (Paul McCartney took over when he left). Various drawings of his have appeared over the years and there has been great interest in his work because of his association with The Beatles.

£1,200-1,600

£350

◄ Signed drawings always fetch more than unsigned ones. John Lennon drew this Christmas card in crayon on a blank double album cover. Unusually, on the reverse he has signed it with a little beetle by his name, which was a popular motif of The Beatles early on in their career. The large size and colour of the drawing make it a particularly attractive display item which will add to its desirability among collectors.

£5,000+

▲ John Lennon's fascination for grotesques is evident in this drawing of a six-headed animal. The headed paper at least doubles its value. The source (Cynthia Lennon) is important because Apple headed paper has been sold in the past making it quite easy to fake such cartoons.

£1,800-2,000

► This pen and ink drawing of *Psychedelic Girls* (c.1967) by John Lennon was one of the many items put up for sale by Cynthia Lennon. It was drawn whilst Lennon was probably under the influence of LSD – the image of the blond-haired girl is typically evocative of the 1960s. Although it has been drawn on a notepad, more time and thought has been spent on it than on many of his other sketches. However, it wasn't drawn for public view – only Lennon's *Bag One* lithographs were drawn to be printed for public sale. This drawing is particularly attractive as a display piece and may appeal to collectors of both rock and pop memorabilia and modern art.

£4,800-5,500

▼ This black ink cartoon self-portrait of Lennon drawn in 1968 is addressed to Paul, a cook who was working at the Academy of the spiritual leader Maharishi Mahesh Yogi, in Rishikesh, India. The Beatles took part in a number of sessions with

Maharishi in 1967-68, learning about meditation and Eastern philosophy, and were with him at a retreat in Wales when they heard about Brian Epstein's death in August 1967. The wording around the portrait refers to Lennon's proposal that Paul should be employed by the group as a chef on his return to England. The drawing is in quite good condition despite slight crease marks down the centre and is a good display item.

£3,200-3,500

▶ John Lennon drew this cartoon specially for a freelance journalist reporting on the court case between Allen Klein versus Apple Records in 1975. Lennon attended the case and became known for his doodling during the hearing. The sheep encircling his signature and the date are a popular Lennon trademark. The drawing is given further provenance by the owner who provided an accompanying letter explaining why Lennon drew the cartoon for him. Drawn in felt pen on lined, buff-coloured paper, it is in good condition and is another fine example of Lennon's work.

£2,000+

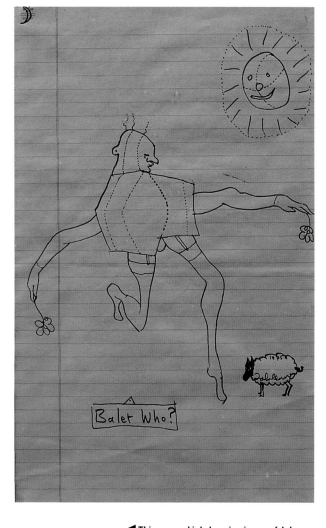

◀ This pen and ink drawing is one of John Lennon's later works. Called *Cowboy Riding A Horse*, it is possibly a self portrait, and is one of a series apparently drawn by Lennon in 1976 while learning Japanese. Pen and ink was Lennon's most common medium, but for his more formal pieces he used silk screens and lithography. His most famous lithographs are the *Bag One* series produced in 1970.

£1,500-2,500

Drawings

Although John Lennon is by far the most prolific artist, drawings by other rock and pop stars do occasionally appear on the market. Probably the greatest output is from Jimi Hendrix, who produced a number of elaborate drawings, some of which are abstract and highly coloured. It is important to establish provenance for his drawings because in recent years some have appeared for sale which are of questionable origin. The drawings on these pages are representative of what else comes on the market besides those produced by The Beatles. Prices in general will be lower than for The Beatles' work, but all of these drawings still provide an interesting and attractive collecting area.

► This ballpoint pen drawing by Michael Jackson entitled "Your Girlfriend" displays a similar high degree of self-portraiture to the drawing by Jackson on the opposite page. It is in good condition and has been signed and dated.

£1,500-2,000

▼ Few cartoons and drawings by Eric Clapton have appeared on the market. This signed self-portrait in black ink (1989) is particularly interesting as it shows in a quick sketch how one of the greatest rock and roll legends sees himself.

£650-750

▼ This pencil sketch by Bob Dylan is not signed but its provenance is confirmed by the fact that it was sold with a number of his lyrics and papers by the couple he lived with in New York in 1961, at the start of his career. Dylan obviously had artistic talent – a self-portrait appears on one of his album covers – but this drawing is simply doodling and as there is nothing to suggest it is by Dylan, it is of modest value – a signature would make it far more attractive.

£800-1,000

▶ This is one of four original sketches of members of The Who drawn by John Entwistle for reproduction on the *Who By Numbers* album sleeve (see p. 22). This example of Pete Townshend is nicknamed "Towser" – other members were known as "Ox", "Dip" and "Barney". The portraits are very desirable as they are signed by Entwistle and were sold by him, and they are the original drawings which appeared on an album cover seen by many thousands of fans.

£1,000+

▲ In recent years a number of drawings by Michael Jackson have appeared on the market which show a high degree of artistic talent and creativity (see opposite). This example has been signed by Jackson and was probably drawn in c.1976. Jackson has openly acknowledged Charlie Chaplin's influence on his career (he dedicated his album *Dangerous* to the comedian), and there is an obvious degree of self-portraiture in this drawing of Chaplin. Because this caricature is in pencil rather than in ink or biro it will last a particularly long time – pencil is one of the most durable media.

£1,500-2,000

Signed Oddities

A vast array of signed oddities appear on the market which often have little or no association with the artist or his music. They tend to be examples of signatures obtained at opportunist signings. Signed menu cards frequently come up for sale, as do cigarette packets and even cigarette cases.

Other signed oddities include official pieces of paper which bear a star's signature, such as cheques and credit card slips, or application forms and questionnaires. In this category John Lennon tends to fetch the highest premium, and those bills for the largest amounts are most desirable. Other items which may be signed by rock and roll stars include promotional clothing: an usherette's Beatles' dress signed by the band and Brian Epstein fetched over £2,000 in 1988.

▼ Sheet music for The Beatles' hits was sold inexpensively to the general public. This example, for the band's first UK number two single hit *Please Please Me*, released in January 1963, has a good image and is signed by each member of the group. Unfortunately, the signatures are not that clear because of the busy background, and Ringo Starr's is barely discernible at all.

£1,000

▼ The Beatles signed this letter of investiture on 26 October 1965 when they went to Buckingham Palace to receive their MBEs. Other items from that day also come on the market, including a number of signed visiting cards.

£900-1,000

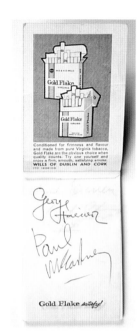

Gold Flake *satisfy!*

▲ The Beatles were bombarded with requests for signatures everywhere they went and to meet demand they even gave out fan club cards with non-genuine signatures signed by their secretaries. It is therefore very important to familiarize oneself with the band's signatures. They signed this small notebook bearing an advertisement for cigarettes whilst in Dublin on their only trip to Eire, in November 1963. Because the notebook has no direct link with the band and the signatures are on two pages, making them difficult to display, the value is lowered. **£600**

▶▶ This Cavern Club membership card was signed by all four members of The Beatles in 1963. Unusually, Ringo has not signed his surname, which suggests he knew the person quite well. The cards were given out to all regular Cavern Club visitors, but any signed cards are very desirable as the Cavern is the venue most associated with the band's early career. Even though the covers are quite worn and the pages where the member's details would have been are missing, the fact that Paul McCartney has signed "The Beatles" will add a premium. Several membership cards have come up for sale, but very few from 1963, The Beatles' last year at the Club.

£1,000-1,5000

▼ This genuine and clear set of Beatles' signatures is one of the best examples to be found and provides a good basis with which to compare other Beatles signatures for authenticity. The relatively worn condition of the page is typical, but because the signatures are so legible this set is worth around £400 even though the document itself is uninteresting.

▶ This page of a shooting script from a Morecambe and Wise television show in 1963 has been signed by The Beatles and Morecambe and Wise. The dedication "To Paul" refers to Paul Kossoff (later to be the lead guitarist of Free), who was a great fan of the group and whose father, actor David Kossoff was rehearsing in the next studio to the band at the time. The fact that the document is dated and mentions The Beatles in the text adds to its value. The page was sold by David Kossoff himself.

£1,500

AUTOGRAPHS

Autographs appear regularly on the market and the price for The Beatles' autographs in particular has jumped considerably in the last two or three years as sources of their signature have begun to run out. They tend to fetch around a minimum of £400, and may be bought framed with something else associated with the band such as an album sleeve or photograph, in order to make them more attractive display pieces. Aside from The Beatles, very few other artists are important enough for their signatures to be worth a similar figure if on an autograph book page. Autographs of The Rolling Stones tend to fetch around £200-300, and those of Buddy Holly and the Crickets and Jimi Hendrix are collectable; but very few others would sell on their own. Condition is important as any damage must not interfere with the signature: signs of age, however, add to authenticity.

◄ Elvis Presley appeared at the Hilton Hotel in Las Vegas on 13 separate occasions in the 1970s and performed there 21 times. Menus were made commemorating his visits, and this example has been signed by Elvis in ball point pen. The signature is clear but, like much Elvis material, this item is surprisingly inexpensive.

£250-300

▼ Jimi Hendrix has signed this Fender guitar string packet with a typical inscription to a female fan. Although the packet is ostensibly a very ordinary piece of paper, the fact that

the string is for the make of guitar Hendrix used makes it more interesting to the collector.

£650-750

► Some of the more unusual items to come up for sale are these three wooden spoons and a tin baking tray which were all signed by John Lennon and Yoko Ono when they were at a showing at the ICA in London of a collection of their very avant-garde films (when they were tied up in a large white bag). These items were handed out to the audience for them to make a noise during the showing of *Two Virgins*. Several examples of the spoons and tins have appeared on the market in recent years as the owners have begun to recognize their potential value.

£600-800

▼ Noel Redding, bass guitarist with the Jimi Hendrix Experience, sold this passport himself, and has added under his photograph the inscription "We certainly did travel". Every page is crammed full of entry and exit visas which makes it a very interesting biographical document, as it is possible to trace the band's tours through its pages.

£700-800

▲ As with the guitar string packet opposite, Jimi Hendrix has signed this HMV record shop paper bag with an inscription to a female fan – "love always". The bag comes complete with the receipt for the record which was inside the bag, dated 20 May 1967, which places the signature in an historical context.

*Because Jimi Hendrix has written fewer words on this bag than on the guitar string packet the value is less.

◀ The British costume designer Julie Harris worked on the costumes for The Beatles' film *A Hard Days' Night* in 1964. This sketch for the film has been signed by Harris and all four members of the band whom she met during the production of the film at the Scala Theatre in London. It is particularly desirable as it is large and attractive, is in excellent condition, shows The Beatles' signatures clearly, and is closely associated with the band.

£450-500

£2,500

▼ The message on this white cotton pillow slip from the Dorchester Hotel in London bears a rather poignant message from Michael Jackson to his supporters. The pillow case was thrown down to his fans in the street during his visit to London in 1991. *It is possible that following all the recent controversy surrounding Michael Jackson the prices for items signed by him will increase.
*A napkin from a hotel in Belgium bearing almost exactly the same words has also appeared for sale at a recent auction.

£400-500

▲ Even cars have been signed by rock stars. This Czech-built Trabant, made in 1982, has been signed on the bonnet by members of U2 and was sold as part of a radio station promotional campaign in Dublin to raise money for a local drug centre. The car has become synonymous with the band; it appears on *Achtung Baby* and was used as part of U2's stage set on a recent world tour. It is in full working order, but because it is such an unusual item it is impossible to suggest a price.

► This huge Stratocaster-style guitar was used in the promotional video, *Can't Stop This Thing We Started*

(1992). At 166in (420cm) long and 52in (132cm) high, it is probably the largest guitar ever built. It was used as a bucking bronco for Bryan Adams during his performance in the video. It has been signed by Adams and although it is inscribed to the Hard Rock Café, it was never actually given to them. When it was sold at a London auction in 1992 it fetched £6,600, five times its estimate.

▼ John Lennon and Yoko Ono filled in these amusing questionnaires while on a BOAC flight from London to Nassau on 24 May 1969. The cartoon annotations and comments by the couple

provide an interesting insight into their characters. In excellent condition, they are fine display pieces.

£2,500+

► This Premier Everplay tambourine has been signed, dated and inscribed by Phil Collins and is accompanied by his characteristic cartoon self-portrait. It was used by Collins during his performance at the Live Aid concert in 1985 at Wembley, London. He flew out on Concorde immediately afterwards to appear in a Live Aid concert in the United States in the evening. The tambourine was probably donated for sale to raise money for charity and in recent years several items

donated by Phil Collins for charity have appeared at auction.

£200-300

▼ David Bowie's signature is rare, as when he is not on stage he is a very private person. Consequently, any-

thing that does come on the market is immediately attractive to collectors. This top copy of an Amex bill is particularly interesting as it is signed in Bowie's real name, David R. Jones, and gives the place and the date it was signed.

£100-150

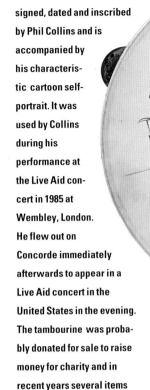

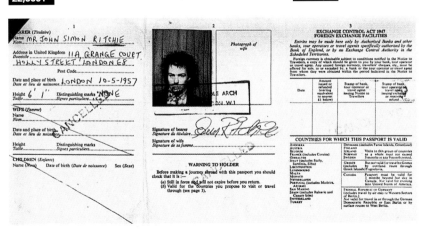

▲ This British visitor's passport for Sid Vicious is in his true name of John Simon Ritchie. The photograph presents a fittingly punk-like image of the star and is accompanied by his signature and personal details. He tried unsuccessfully to use it to travel to America. **£1,400-1,600**

Presentation Discs and Awards

Presentation discs are awarded by record industries in recognition of levels of sales of singles or albums, and although the number of records sold to qualify for such awards varies from country to country, the three levels of certification – silver, gold or platinum – are universally used. They are popular because although they cannot be played, they are attractive display items. Because of the high value of discs awarded to the most successful artists, counterfeits – particularly of American awards – do appear on the market. The most obvious way to confirm authenticity is to ensure that the design coincides with that in use at the time the single or album was certified – American awards have undergone specific changes over the years (see pp. 60-61) which makes them immediately dateable.

Some awards are presented in recognition of achievement, rather than number of records sold. These are given out in far fewer numbers than presentation discs and there is usually only one example of each award made, so they tend to command considerably higher prices (duplicate presentation discs can be ordered from an officially appointed supplier). These awards are considered more prestigious than a sales award, and the recipient is much less likely to allow it out of his possession. Nevertheless, some are given away as gifts or souvenirs, and these are the ones that subsequently become available to collectors.

Only very rare and expensive recordings and pressings are sold through auction houses (eg unreleased acetates or those with an extremely limited circulation). But there is a vast amount of vinyl sold in second hand record shops, records fairs and through specialist magazines. The recent decline in the production of vinyl records as the CD and MC cassette become more popular has led to a series of somewhat misleading articles in the press regarding the potential increase in value of some vinyl discs. However, of the millions of records available, only a few are of any significant value. To help the collector, several useful price guides have been published, but these have to limit themselves in the categories they cover. Also, prices quoted are for any examples in mint condition, and these are likely to be the current maximum.

Recordings and pressings in limited circulation are highly sought-after. Two famous examples are the Sex Pistols' withdrawn A&M single *God Save The Queen/No Feelings*, a hundred of which were allegedly saved from destruction (these are now worth around £800, compared to £5 for the ordinary version on Virgin); and The Rolling Stones' *The Promotional Album,* of which 200 copies of the American run of 400 came into the United Kingdom (these are worth around £600 today).

In some cases a variation from the ordinary of the sleeve or label design may make a record particularly collectable. Current estimates for two Beatles records in this category (see p. 71) place them among the most valuable records released to date.

When buying any recording or pressing condition is absolutely vital, and to help potential buyers a leading UK magazine has devised a grading system, now used by collectors worldwide, which lists seven levels of condition ranging from "mint" to "bad" and describes the physical appearance of both sleeve and label and the sound quality of the recording.

Left: A rare custom-made presentation gold disc for Cold Sweat – Part 1, *for James Brown's million-seller.*

Above: An album cover for The Rolling Stones' Sticky Fingers, *Rolling Stones Records.*

Presentation Discs

The Recording Industry Association of America (RIAA) began presenting awards in 1958, and the British Pop Industry (BPI) in 1976. They are awarded to rock and pop stars in recognition of the number of records sold. The target levels for which they are awarded are the same, irrespective of the artist concerned. There is an accepted hierarchy in the collectability of presentation discs: most collectable are discs awarded to a particular artist; then, discs awarded to people associated with the production; next, discs awarded to the record company for whom the artist works; and finally, those awarded to anyone else involved, such as a radio station who may have promoted the record. Today, particularly in the United States, presentation discs are handed out in large numbers, whereas in the 1960s the number was far lower. Discs from the 1960s tend to be more desirable, and those presented to The Beatles by far the most collectable and most expensive. Elton John, The Rolling Stones, Prince and Eric Clapton are also very sought-after names on awards. Generally, the more records an artist has sold and the bigger the star is, the more collectable the award will be. Awards from Britain and the United States are the most collectable as they represent the biggest markets for records in the world; next are Japan, Canada and Australia, then the countries in Northern Europe.

▼ Platinum discs were introduced in 1976. Whereas those awarded in the United Kingdom were silver in colour, American discs were gold.
*This American Floater disc was awarded to John Lennon for sales of over a million of The Beatles' last single *Let It Be* (1970).
*From 1964 to 1967 all awards presented to members of The Beatles, even those to Brian Epstein, were inscribed to "The Beatles", rather than to individuals.

▲ This gold Floater disc has been presented to the record company rather than the pop star. Because the award is far-removed from the artist it is significantly less collectable than one awarded to an individual.

£4,000

£800-1,000

◀ This Strip-Plate gold award for John Lennon's LP *Imagine* (1971) was presented by the RIAA to the record producer, Phil Spector, for sales of over 500,000 copies. Because the disc bears both Lennon's and Spector's name it is particularly collectable. Spector first worked with The Beatles on the album *Let It Be* which was very different from the music produced by the band under George Martin.

£2,000

BRITISH AWARDS

British awards have changed very little in style over the years – the basic design is the same as when the first British discs came out in the mid 1970s. In contrast, those from the United States vary greatly (see pp. 60-61). Presentation discs are now changing in Britain and the United States as people are getting awards for CD sales and some awards are given for disc, cassette and CD sales combined. As the market changes vinyl awards will become a thing of the past and are likely to increase in value in the future.

▶ This gold Floater disc was presented to The Beatles for selling over 500,000 copies of *Magical Mystery Tour* (1967) in the United States. This disc was awarded for the LP version which was released in 1976.

£6,500

▲ This White Matte gold disc was presented by the RIAA to The Beatles for their single *I Want To Hold Your Hand* after selling one million copies. Because it is a very rare disc, is in the early style, and is for The Beatles' first US number one hit this is an extremely desirable item among collectors.

£6,500

AMERICAN PRESENTATION DISCS

Green Felt (1958–c.1962) A gold-plated metal disc, set against a background of green felt-like material, in an unpainted wood frame which contained an engraved metal plate inscribed "RIAA". These discs were given out in very small quantities and are very rare.

White Matte (1962–1974) A gold-plated metal disc, set against an off-white linen material background, in an unpainted wooden frame with a gold inner trim. The metal plate with the RIAA logo is placed to the right, and awards for albums had a miniature cover of the LP in the lower left-hand corner. A single/EP must have sold over 1,000,000 copies, an album over $1,000,000 worth, to gain an award.

Floater (1975–1981) A gold-plated record, set against a dark background. Although the dedication plate was engraved, the "Presented To" and RIAA logo were silk-screened. The record and award plate seem to float between the background and the glass in an unpainted frame, hence the name. Miniature reproductions of the cover were included for LP awards. A single must have sold over 1,000,000 copies, an album over 500,000.

▶ This Strip-Plate gold award was presented to Elvis Presley for his album, *Elvis Golden Records Volume 2* for sales over 500,000. The full title – *Fifty Million Elvis Fans Can't Be Wrong* – has been shortened as it could not fit on the label. It was presented posthumously for an album released in 1959. Elvis sold millions of records before the RIAA began such awards so many discs have been awarded to him at a later date. They do not appear on the market very frequently and are much sought-after by collectors.

£1,200

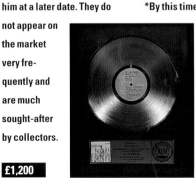

◀ The BPI presented this silver award to Eric Stewart for 10cc's single *I'm Not In Love*. Although the single was released in 1975, this award was not presented until 1976 because this was the first year the BPI awarded silver discs. Stewart was the composer and singer on the single, which reached number one on both sides of the Atlantic.

*On gold discs awarded by the BPI for albums, rather than a reduced-size replica of the album sleeve which appears on the American awards, British awards will often be mounted with a cassette insert. This can be seen on the disc on the facing page awarded to Thin Lizzy. **£400–500**

▶ From 1984 onwards the RIAA began to recognize cassette sales as part of album sales. This Multi-Platinum award was presented to Warner Brothers for sales of over 10 million of Prince's LP, *Purple Rain*, in both album and cassette form. Each million copies sold is represented by a reduction of the album cover.

*By this time RIAA had introduced a hologram into the disc to avoid copying. In the United States there are about six authorized manufacturers of discs so control is difficult – in the United Kingdom there are only two. Check discs very carefully as fakes do appear which look genuine by the use of the right materials, but which give themselves away through small details.

£800–1,000

◀ Sales awards presented to The Rolling Stones or to individual members of the band, although they exist in large numbers, very rarely come up for sale, and usually only filter into the market when sold at a charity event. Consequently they are extremely highly sought-after. This White Matte gold disc was presented to Charlie Watts for sales of over one million of The Rolling Stones' album *Between The Buttons* (1967).

£3,000

▼ This gold award is recognizable as British rather than American by the initials BPI and the Union Jack in the top corner. It was presented to Phonogram for sales worth over £300,000 of Thin Lizzy's album *Bad Reputation* (1977). The limited appeal of the band is reflected in the price. £350

▲ In the 1960s it was popular for pop magazines to hold readers' polls and award discs to the winners. This British award was presented by *Disc* to The Rolling Stones for their single *It's All Over Now*. Although less expensive than official sales awards, because this one is for The Stones it will fetch a premium. £1,500

Platinum Discs From 1976 the RIAA started to award platinum discs. For these awards a single had to sell over 2,000,000 copies, an album over 1,000,000.

Strip-Plate (1982-1984)
A dark background, but the engraving and RIAA logo and miniature cover for album awards were all on the same strip of metal within the frame. Many included a cassette, either in gold or platinum. To qualify for gold, a single must have sold over 1,000,000 copies, an album over 500,000. For platinum a single must have sold over 2,000,000 copies, an album 1,000,000.

Hologram (1985-1989)
Similar to above apart from the RIAA logo, which is within a rainbow-like hologram. Always accompanied by a cassette. For gold a single must have sold over 1,000,000, an album over 500,000; for platinum over 2,000,000 for a single, 1,000,000 for an album.
*From August 1989 the RIAA logo was completely altered and the RIAA seal dropped. There are three different designs: those with a disc; those with a disc and cassette; and those with a disc, cassette and CD. Some now also have customized backgrounds.

◄ Mowtown presented this in-house gold award to Michael Jackson for the album and cassette *Farewell My Summer Love* "For continuing the Jackson legacy", acknowledging Jackson's contribution to the record company. Because this type of award is so rare and Michael Jackson is one of the most successful performers of the 1980s it will command a premium. **£400-500**

◄ Very few discs are actually sold by the artist to whom they are presented. Elton John sold this Floater-style platinum award for his album *A Single Man* at auction as part of a sale of his property. Because Elton John is such a famous artist items connected with him are highly sought-after by collectors. **£2,000**

▲ This Floater disc was awarded to Stevie Nicks for Fleetwood Mac's 1979 album *Tusk* for sales of over 500,000 copies. It was probably Nicks' own copy as she has signed and inscribed the disc; many stars sign discs for charity sales as the potential of rock and pop memorabilia to raise money for funds is realized. **£700-1,000**

◀ This in-house gold disc presented to James Brown by King Records for *Live At The Apollo* was the first award for a live album. When Brown mooted the idea of a live recording in 1962 he received strong opposition but was so determined that he paid for the venture himself. The album was a resounding success and was in the US charts for 66 weeks, selling over a million copies. **£4,000+**

▶ This in-house disc was presented to Larry Nunes by The Beatles in grateful acknowledgement of someone who was instrumental in the group's success. It was presented for the single, *If I Fell*, which was the B side in the United States to the more famous song, *And I Love Her* (1964).

£1,000-1,500

◀ When an artist is presented with a sales award he or she can order subsequent copies for friends and relatives. This silver disc was presented to Madonna for sales of over 60,000 of her album *You Can Dance* (1987). This particular example is inscribed to Great Ormond Street Hospital and was probably ordered by Madonna or the record company to raise money for the hospital.

*The fact that the disc does not have the initials BPI on the plate makes it instantly recognizable as a second pressing or in-house award rather than the original. **£300-400**

IN-HOUSE AWARDS

These are discs which have not been awarded by the official recording industry of the country, but by the record company for whom the artist/artists work, in recognition of record sales. They are easily distinguished from the official sales awards by the missing initials of the recording industry. In-house awards tend to be less collectable than official awards and appear less frequently for sale.

BRITISH DISCS

BPI UK disc sales levels to qualify for a disc (15.12.93)

Singles (up to December 1988)
Silver 250,000
Gold 500,000
Platinum 1,000,000

Singles (after January 1989)
Silver 200,000
Gold 400,000
Platinum 600,000

Albums
Silver 60,000
Gold 100,000
Platinum 300,000

British Awards were first presented in 1976.

Awards

Awards are very personal objects presented to an individual artist or band and because of this they very rarely come onto the open market. Occasionally the star may pass them on to friend or members of his or her family, or they may be sold at auction to raise money for charity. Like presentation discs (see pp. 58-63), awards are a visual representation of the success of a particular artist. They usually take the form of plaques, and occasionally, statuettes. Far fewer awards were given out in the 1960s than today, and a number of important bands have received many more awards since they disbanded than when they were together. However, despite the number of awards presented to The Beatles, few appear on the market and any that do are much prized by collectors.

▶ The Ivor Novello award is the most prestigious British Award for songwriters, and is the highest recognition from the recording industry of a composer's achievements. John Lennon was presented with this award in 1963 for writing the song *She Loves You*. Like many of his personal possessions the award was sold at auction by Cynthia Lennon.

£7,000-8,000

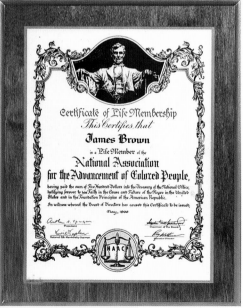

◀ James Brown's influence on soul music has been phenomenal, making him a legend in his own time. This Certificate of Life Membership of the National Association for the Advancement of Colored People was presented to James Brown in May 1966. It is important because James Brown made his membership of this association public in an attempt to show his support for, and interest in black issues. Although not specifically related to his music, it reflects something very close to the artist's heart and therefore is still collectable.

£3,000+

▶ This highly acclaimed American Music Award was presented to Michael Jackson in 1984 for his best-selling album *Thriller*. It is accompanied by a photograph of Jackson receiving the award which confirms its authenticity. The award is inscribed "Favorite Album Pop/Rock Thriller Michael Jackson". Because it is a unique and highly personal possession of a such a major star the award will command a premium.

* *Thriller* was the biggest selling pop album to date

and a record seven tracks from it have reached the US top ten singles chart since its release.

£1,500-1,800

▲ Ampex, manufacturers of recording tape, have presented many awards over the years to studios who used their product to record successful records. This Ampex Golden Reel Award was presented to Rampart Studios for The Who's album, *Who Are You?* (1978). Awards such as these are rarely offered for sale and are not as desirable as those associated with a particular musician or band.

£80-120

▶ The National Academy of Recording Arts and Sciences (NARAS) gives awards which are the musical equivalent of the "Oscar" film awards. This NARAS award was presented to Lennon and McCartney in recognition of their single *Hey Jude* as "Song of the Year" in 1968. Because the inscription on the award is specifically made out to two members of The Beatles it is worth significantly more than if only one member of the band were mentioned.

£1,500-1,600

▶ The German magazine *Bravo* (no longer in existence) presented this "silver" award to Ringo Starr in the 1968. Its provenance is secure as it once belonged to the group's road manager, Mal Evans.

£450-550

Recordings and Pressings

This section deals mainly with acetates but also covers promotional records, factory samples, records which have some mistake on the label which makes them unusual, and mis-pressings (for example, both sides of a record pressed with the same song). An acetate is a rough proof of a record cut in the studio directly from a demonstration tape, and as such is a working copy of the record. The most valuable Beatles acetates are those with versions of a well-known song which has never been heard before, or a song never released. Acetates were only made in very limited numbers, but a surprising amount do come on the market, sometimes turning up in second-hand record shops, discarded as part of an unwanted collection. They are usually given away to friends and relatives of the band and most have gradually filtered into the market through these channels.

▼ This is an exceptionally rare and highly sought-after edition of The Beatles' album, *Please Please Me* – in stereo and with the gold and black label, which was only available for two to three weeks (after which time the label was changed to black and yellow). Most examples were produced in mono; if this edition is in mint condition and comes complete with its album sleeve it will be worth £1,000, whereas a mono version will only fetch £150.

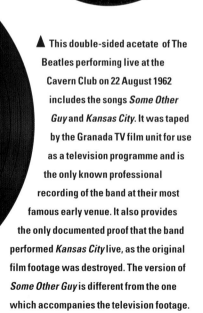

▲ This double-sided acetate of The Beatles performing live at the Cavern Club on 22 August 1962 includes the songs *Some Other Guy* and *Kansas City*. It was taped by the Granada TV film unit for use as a television programme and is the only known professional recording of the band at their most famous early venue. It also provides the only documented proof that the band performed *Kansas City* live, as the original film footage was destroyed. The version of *Some Other Guy* is different from the one which accompanies the television footage.

£16,000-18,000

▶ All Beatles' promotional discs are collectable, but this example, with the red A label, for The Beatles' first single *Love Me Do/PS I Love You*, is the most sought-after. At this early stage in the band's career it is interesting to note the mis-spelling of Paul's surname, as "McArtney". The record originally came in a picture sleeve and examples in mint condition and complete with the cover will fetch over £1,000.

£500

CONDITION

Condition is very important with acetates; they are made of aluminium coated with a very thin layer of vinyl, which can easily become damaged. They were not designed to have a long life and were only intended to be played a few times. Acetates from the 1960s tend to be scratched and the sound quality is quite poor. However, if the music differs significantly from the final version, they will still be valuable, particularly if they feature major artists. Auction houses always provide a cassette recording of the acetate, which is sold with it, in order for prospective purchasers to be able to hear the recording without actually playing the disc itself. As the production of an acetate is a relatively simple process, care should be taken when buying, as fakes do exist, especially of Beatles' tracks.

▼ This 7-inch double-sided acetate of *Fixing A Hole* from the *Sergeant Pepper* album is on the white Emidisc label used for Beatles' acetates. RM3 means it is the third mono remix, but there is little difference between this and the final version. By the time *Sergeant Pepper* was released, acetates had been produced at many different stages; all of these are collectable.   £500+

▲ The label on this Emidisc acetate of *Lucy In The Sky With Diamonds* gives good historical information which makes it particularly collectable. PMc does not stand for Paul McCartney, but for Phil McDonald, the tape operator at Abbey Road who cut the acetate.

£750

◀ This double-sided 7-inch acetate of Queen's second single release in the United Kingdom *Killer Queen/Flick Of The Wrist* is very similar to the final released version (October 1974). However, following the death of Freddie Mercury there has been a renewed interest in Queen material, and consequently this acetate will be sought-after by collectors.

£160-200

▶ Vinyl proofs of records, called test pressings, are produced to make sure the recording sounds as intended. These are less valuable than acetates because, musically, they are the same as the final recorded version (although there are differences in the label). This 78rpm test-pressing of *Jailhouse Rock* (1957) is in mint condition and is one of only a few available. A collector will be paying for the fact that the disc is physically, rather than musically different, from the released version.

£150-200

▲ Acetates which are among some of the earliest recordings of a band or artist always command a premium. This 78rpm double-sided acetate has versions of Roy Orbison's first recordings, *Ooby Dooby* and *Hey Miss Fanny*, which were recorded at the Norman Petty Studios in the United States in 1955, where Buddy Holly recorded his music later on. Roy Orbison has undergone a revival in popularity in recent years because much of his old material has been re-released posthumously.

£1,000-1,500

▶ This single-sided 7-inch acetate was cut from an early demonstration tape in 1964 when The Who were performing as The High Numbers. *I'm The Face* (July 1964) was the only single released by them under this name.

£150-160

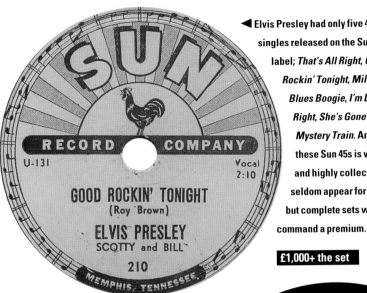

◀ Elvis Presley had only five 45rpm singles released on the Sun record label; *That's All Right*, *Good Rockin' Tonight*, *Milkcow Blues Boogie*, *I'm Left, You're Right, She's Gone* and *Mystery Train*. Any one of these Sun 45s is very rare and highly collectable. They seldom appear for sale singly but complete sets will command a premium.

£1,000+ the set

▶ Factory samples were made either as vinyl or, more rarely, as acetates, for similar purposes to a test pressing. This double-sided 12-inch acetate factory sample of *The Golden B Sides* was never actually released by The Rolling Stones. This makes it a particularly interesting and desirable collector's piece.

£480-550

◀ This 7-inch single-sided acetate of The Beatles' *Strawberry Fields* is one of only four cut on 16 December 1966 by Abbey Road engineer Ron Pender. It is markedly different from the final version and as such is a highly important item.

£900-1,000

COLLECTING

Beatles acetates are by far the most desirable and expensive to collect. Even an example with no discernible difference from the finished recording may fetch £250. Apart from The Beatles, collecting is confined to the big names such as Roy Orbison and The Who, and earlier artists, rather than Michael Jackson and Madonna. Nowadays, acetates are far less important in the recording studio as modern technology has taken over.

Some acetates are not expensive. Value is directly related to how different the music may be to the final version – those most different are the most desirable. Value is also determined by the detail on the label. Research on The Beatles is so refined that an acetate can be pinned down to a specific time on a specific day, even if there is no date on the label. Singles and albums are usually one-sided, although later ones use both sides.

Album Sleeves and Proofs

Albums sleeves are only collectable if they are rare or unusual. One prime example is the sleeve for John and Yoko's *Two Virgins* album (1968) – the full-frontal nude photograph caused an uproar when it appeared on the shelves and prompted calls for it to be withdrawn; as a compromise it was subsequently sold, with the sleeve, but in a brown paper bag! Examples of this sleeve for a mono recording are worth up to £800, whilst those with a stereo recording can fetch around a quarter of the price. Album sleeves and artwork are an artform in their own right and fetch high prices.

◄ Any examples of original artwork are very rare; those which vary slightly from the final version are particularly collectable, as are examples of a very striking and famous image. The design of this original photomontage artwork appeared on both the 7-inch and 12-inch single covers of David Bowie's record, *Fashion* (1980), and because it is such a well-known design it will be much sought-after.

£1,000-1,200

▲ The original artwork for the sleeve of Supertramp's album *Crisis What Crisis?* (1975) is particularly important as the album sold 4.6 million copies worldwide until 1992, and it is still selling well today. Consequently it is an easily recognizable and highly collectable image. Generally, the more famous the album, the more money the artwork will fetch. Most designs are produced by an unknown designer in the production studio, and people are paying for what the image represents rather than the art itself.

£2,000+

▼ ▶ The artwork on the right for the cover of The Beatles album *Yesterday And Today* is known as the "butcher" design. When the album was released with this cover in the United States Capitol withdrew it as they felt it was offensive. Copies were sent back to the factory and a new "trunk" cover pasted over the top (see below). Most collectable is the original "butcher" cover in a stereo version (around £2,000), because these are almost non-existent

whereas the final "trunk" version is of little value at all. The original artworks to the sleeves featured here are worth around £200-300 each.

▼ Several proofs were produced for the sleeve of the Sex Pistols' notorious album *Never Mind The Bollocks, Here's The Sex Pistols* (1977), all of which are visually striking. This example was sold together with a proof for *God Save Sex Pistols*, which was an alternative title for the album. Unusually, both these proofs have been signed by the designer, Jamie Reid, who originated this now-famous style of "blackmail-note" design. **£850-1,000 the pair**

▼ Although this famous "dress" cover design for David Bowie's album, *The Man Who Sold The World*, was released by Mercury, it

was not available in the United States. Because the sleeve is so rare, examples in mint condition with the record intact will fetch up to £250; examples of the RCA sleeve released in the United States later are only worth around £12.

£150

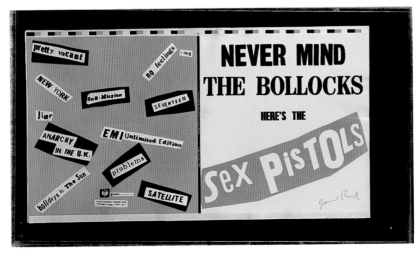

Clothing

Some rock and pop stars are as well known for their clothes as they are for their music. The more distinctive and identifiable the clothing is with its owner the more collectable it tends to be. Many articles have achieved an almost iconic status because they have featured prominently in a star's career and have come to represent the artist himself.

Modern superstars such as Prince and Madonna incorporate a great deal of theatre into their live performances, and their highly individual clothing, often designed exclusively for them, is essential to the show. Many of Madonna's costumes are designed by Jean Paul Gaultier, undoubtedly one of Europe's most innovative fashion designers.

Flamboyant or outrageous clothing is nothing new

in popular music. Little Richard and James Brown in the 1950s were way ahead of their time when they wore lamé suits, bouffant hairstyles and make-up. Their look was remarkable when placed within the context of the late 1950s and early 1960s when most pop stars dressed in suits and ties and appeared little different from their audiences. One only has to look at the styles adopted by the British musicians in the "glam-rock" movement of the early 1970s, and Prince a decade later, to see how far-reaching their influence has been.

In contrast to such flamboyant clothing are those articles which have become distinct because of their ordinariness. Perhaps the best examples are Buddy Holly's horn-rimmed glasses. More part of the boy-next-door look than that associated with rock and roll, a pair of his glasses fetched a world record price when sold at auction in the United States in 1990.

The role of pop star as fashion trend-setter was probably given the greatest impetus by The Beatles. They took the world of musical performance by storm and influenced it in a way that not even Elvis Presley had achieved. The styles The Beatles wore in the 1960s – from the Pierre Cardin-inspired, round-necked, collarless jackets and Chelsea boots of 1963 to the psychedelic fashions of 1967 – were widely copied, and it therefore not

surprising that collectors will now pay high prices for original garments.

Authenticity is a prime consideration. Some items of clothing have become so familiar that they have become their own stamp of authenticity. If the clothing is less distinctive collectors should look for other proof of ownership. There may be photographs or footage of an artist wearing the item, or a written statement from the person who acquired it, assuring collectors of its origin and giving facts about times, people and places which can be checked. Also of help are original makers' labels inside the garment, because some costumiers may be able to provide documentation of the garment's purchase.

Originality of condition is important when buying clothing because an article may pass through several hands over the years and undergo alterations which will drastically reduce its value. This does not mean condition has to be pristine – a costume which looks like it has been well-worn, or at least not brand new, is far more interesting to the collector. Any clothing imbued with the performer's persona is also at a premium. For example, a shirt worn by Sid Vicious is likely to be worth far more if it is dirty and torn than if it were perfect.

Left: A Pop Art plastic stage suit designed by Bob Mackie for Elton John, 1986.
Above: An embroidered black cotton piano motif stage suit designed by Bob Mackie for Elton John, 1980.

1950s and 1960s

There is relatively little clothing around today from the 1950s mainly because stage costume as a concept in rock and roll was only just developing. Buddy Holly is the only artist from the 1950s whose clothes have appeared on the market in any quantity and this is largely because his family held a sale of his possessions at auction in the United States in 1990. With a few exceptions – such as Elvis Presley – most artists wore everyday clothes on stage and these tended to be rather conservative suits and ties. Because 1950s' clothing is so rare today, any that does come up for sale is generally expensive and highly desirable.

Among artists who were performing in the 1960s John Lennon is the one whose clothing appears on the market most frequently. Few items worn by Paul McCartney have ever come up for sale, although at some of the very first rock and pop auctions in London a number of The Beatles' famous stage suits were offered, but never a full set belonging to the four Beatles.

► The fact that this black felt Homburg belonged to John Lennon is confirmed because it was sold by his housekeeper. In addition, there is a photograph that shows Lennon wearing a similar hat during the recording of the *Sergeant Pepper* album in 1967. Because there is no label saying that this is Lennon's hat the price is considerably lower than for something that can be immediately identified as belonging to him.

£700-900

▼ This brown suede jacket was worn by John Lennon on the cover of The Beatles' *Rubber Soul* album released in 1965. Because it is such a famous article of clothing it is highly sought-after.

£15,000-20,000

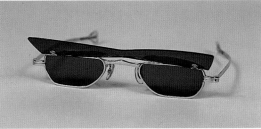

▲ John Lennon acquired this pair of sunglasses whilst on tour in Japan. They were sold by Lennon's housekeeper, and further provenance is provided by several photographs which show him wearing the glasses.

£1,700–1,900

▼ Military-style jackets were a popular trend in the late 1960s among rock stars and the general public. This example was worn by John Lennon in 1967 prior to the famous military jackets worn by The Beatles on the *Sergeant Pepper* sleeve.

£12,000–15,000

▲ Before The Beatles' image was smartened up by their manager Brian Epstein, the band, influenced by their tours to Germany, wore leather trousers and leather jackets. John Lennon frequently wore this leather jacket on stage between 1960 and 1962 and photographs taken in the Cavern Club show the band in similar clothing.

£27,000

▼ These cotton armbands were issued to The Beatles and their entourage to wear during their Japanese tour in 1966. This particular pair was worn by the photographer on the tour, Robert Whitaker. None of the others have yet appeared on the market, but a photograph taken by Whitaker shows John Lennon wearing his. The items will have a strong appeal to the Japanese.

£900–1,000

▼ This shirt worn by John Lennon was designed by The Fool who also produced a number of psychedelic items for The Beatles' Apple shop in London (see pp. 118-121). It was sold by Les Anthony, John's former chauffeur and body guard, accompanied by a letter confirming its authenticity.

£1,200-1,500

◄ Jimi Hendrix's flamboyant image mirrored his performances. The nylon scarf and jewelry on this " Westerner" hat is typical of his style. The hat was Hendrix's trademark; he wore it constantly until 1968 and was photographed with it for the cover of *Smash Hits* (1967).

£14,000+

► Clothes not actually owned by a star but produced commercially as souvenirs are far less valuable because they were usually made in large numbers. The Beatles' animated film *Yellow Submarine* inspired numerous pieces of merchandise, but because this particular outfit of a cotton T-shirt and shorts is so rare it is highly sought-after. It was made by Collegeville Costumes in 1968 as part of a set of Halloween outfits.

£300-400

▼ John Lennon bought this Middle-Eastern velvet robe while he was on holiday in Greece in 1967. Despite the fact that Lennon was never seen wearing the robe in public it is still highly collectable.

*The robe was a part of the collection sold by his former wife, Cynthia Lennon, at an auction in 1991, so the provenance is cast-iron.

£3,000-4,000

▲ This hand-painted silk jacket was one of only a handful made by a female designer in London who specialized in silk ties. It belonged to Mitch Mitchell, drummer with the Jimi Hendrix Experience. Hendrix's similar jacket featured an eye motif. The jacket is an evocative example of the fashions of the time and although Mitchell is perhaps not a household name, because he was part of such an important rock band this jacket is highly collectable. **£10,000-12,000**

◄ The Beatles made the "Chelsea" boot popular in the 1960s. This pair was bought by John Lennon at Anello & Davide in London. The fact that the boots are well worn makes them more appealing and will increase their value. **£3,000-4,000**

▼ Any item of clothing worn by a major artist on the cover of an album is immediately highly collectable. The successful female group The Supremes wore these black silk crêpe dresses on the back cover of their album *Funny Girl* (1968). Each dress is embroidered with the initial of the star, associating them with the artist.

£1,100-1,200 the set

▶ This bottle green frock coat and white cotton ruff shirt are typical of the "Regency gentleman" look The Kinks adopted in c.1964 when bands were just beginning to develop a stronger image. (The Kinks released *Dedicated Follower Of Fashion* in 1966.) Kinks' material has made very few appearances at auction and prices are at a premium.

£1,700-1,800

▶ Normally, black performers in the 1960s wore formal suits, so James Brown's penchant for wearing unusual eye-catching outfits was quite exceptional. This stage coat is accompanied by a photograph from the album *The James Brown Show*, 1967, showing him wearing the coat.

£2,500-3,000

▶ Elvis Presley wore this satin boxing robe in 1962 on the film *Kid Galahad* in which he played the title role. Elvis' clothing from the early 1960s appears on the market far less frequently than that worn on and off stage in the 1970s (see pp. 86-87).

£6,000-8,000

▲ This coat was worn by Elvis' manager Colonel Tom Parker to promote Elvis Presley's film *Girls! Girls ! Girls !* (1962). It has a dual appeal because after its promotional use it was presented as a gift to Mal Evans – a keen fan of Elvis – when The Beatles met the star and The Colonel at Elvis' house in North Hollywood in August 1965. It was sold together with a photograph of The Colonel signing the coat while Mal is actually wearing it which places the article in a historical context.

£4,000-5,000

▶ This peacock feather waist-coat is typical of the distinctive clothes Jimi Hendrix liked to wear on stage. (He also had a penchant for feather boas). A photograph showing Hendrix wearing the waistcoat on stage at the Fillmore East in May 1968 confirms its authenticity.

£8,000-12,000

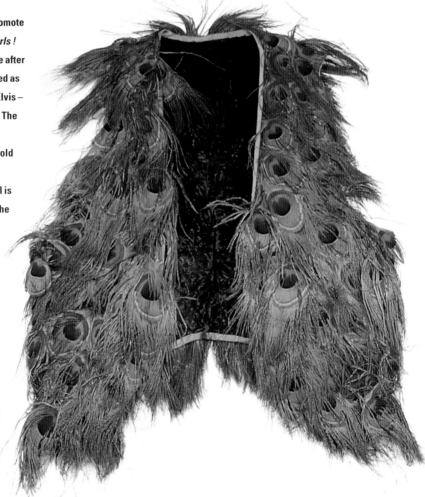

▼ A collection of clothing worn by Ray Fenwick of The Spencer Davis Group was offered for sale in 1989. Although not as collectable individually, this selection provides a colourful record of rock and roll in the late 1960s.

£500+

▲ Buddy Holly's bow tie is one of his most famous trademarks. He wore it throughout his career and because this is the only one he owned, it is highly collectable.

£3,500-4,000

▲ Suede shoes such as these owned by Buddy Holly have strong associations with the 1950s' rock and roll image (Elvis Presley sang *Blue Suede Shoes* in 1956). They were an integral part of his stage costume and two other pairs have come up for sale in recent years. *Buddy Holly had a preference for expensive Italian- made clothing.

£600-800

◀ Early Elvis clothing that appears on the market tends to be from his appearances in films rather than from his performances on stage. Elvis wore this particular striped T-shirt in MGM's *Jailhouse Rock* in 1957 and inside it is a studio label with his name on. The shirt was originally won in a competition held by the women's magazine *Mirabelle* in 1957.

*Several magazines in the 1950s offered items of clothing worn by celebrities as prizes – for example, Marylin Monroe's blouse from the 1956 film *Bus Stop* was offered.

£3,000-4,000

▼ When Buddy Holly wore his prescription glasses on stage he paved the way for other stars to follow suit. This pair was worn by Buddy Holly later on in his career, when he preferred squarer frames than his earlier Rayban look. They sold for $45,000 (£30,000) at auction in New York in 1990 and broke the world record for a piece of rock and roll clothing. Few items are as instantly recognizable.

£30,000+

▲ Buddy Holly was a keen leather worker (He also tooled a guitar cover – see p. 98). He made this belt in 1954/5 and because it is so closely associated with him demand for it will be very high.

*The few examples of his work that have appeared display a great talent for a craft not generally linked to this rock and roll legend.

£1,300-1,500

1970s – Elton John

Elton John was arguably the most successful and flamboyant artist of the 1970s, and was the world's number one rock and roll performer until he was overtaken by Michael Jackson in the 1980s. He is particularly famous for his fantastic and often breathtaking stage attire. The elaborate nature of his stage wardrobe can be gauged by the fact that he needed a separate flight case purely to carry his glasses! It is not surprising then that much of his clothing has appeared on the market, particularly as he held a sale of memorabilia in 1988 that included dozens of different costumes. Because they are all designer "one-offs" they are difficult to value, but each one is so distinctive that prices will always be high.

◄ On several occasions Elton John had costumes specially designed to match the venue at which he was performing. This Dodger Stadium suit was made for his performance at the baseball stadium in October 1975 – it even comes complete with a baseball bat! *Other novelty costumes made for Elton John include one resembling the Statue of Liberty and a Stars and Stripes outfit. *Like many of Elton John's stage costumes, this outfit was designed by Bob Mackie.

£7,000+

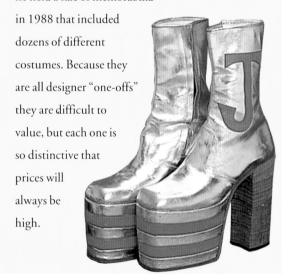

◄ Platform boots were very much a part of Elton John's 1970s stage image. Although they were a phenomenon made popular by the short-lived glam-rock music, Elton John's were amongst the highest and most outrageous. This monogramed pair has 6¼in (16cm) heels and a 4⅛in (10.5cm) platform.

£5,000+

▼ Another example of Elton John's footware is this pair of scarlet platform shoes with a rainbow diamanté design on the heels (3½in/9cm) and platforms (1¼in/3cm). Like a number of other pairs owned by Elton they were designed by Ferradini. Another similar pair has simulated pearl toecaps.

£3,000+

► This 1970 suit designed by Annie Reavie was Elton John's first professionally-made outfit and is very modest when compared to later costumes. The fact that the blouson is lettered "Elton" will add to its value because it immediately identifies the suit with a specific rock star.

£1,200-1,500

▼ Elton John had many pairs of glasses, usually fitted with prescription lenses. Each pair is highly individual and many display Elton's sense of humour. This pair in the shape of grand pianos is typical– others were in the shape of the American flag, a bicycle and Mickey Mouse. Because they are such a strong part of his image they fetch particularly high prices.

£2,000-10,000 a pair

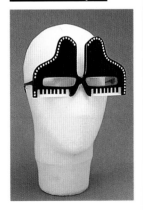

COLLECTING

Much of Elton John's clothing has been bought by the Hard Rock Café chain and can be seen displayed on the walls of their various branches throughout the world. Other items are bought by specific companies to promote their products – the makers of "Doc Marten's" bought Elton's giant boots worn in the film *Tommy*, and several pairs of his glasses have been acquired by spectacle retailers. However, Elton John also has a large number of loyal fans who buy his clothes for their own collections.

▲ Elton John's most flamboyant costumes tend to fetch the highest prices. This suit designed in c.1973 is worth around twice as much as the one illustrated on the right. It was worn at the time of the release of his album *Goodbye Yellow Brick Road* when he was at he pinnacle of his career, both as a musician and a showman.

£2,500-3,000

1970s – Others

Platform shoes, flared trousers and jumpsuits dominate the fashions of the early 1970s. Apart from Elton John's costumes (see pp. 82-83), some of the stars from the 1970s whose clothing has appeared on the market include Elvis Presley, Marc Bolan, The Jacksons and John Lennon. However, Elvis's clothes have commanded some of the highest prices and a number of his distinctive outfits have appeared at auction over the years.

◄ **Marc Bolan shed his late 1960s' hippie persona to emerge as one of glam-rock's leading exponents. This pair of gold lamé dungarees, labelled Alkasura (a shop in London's King's Road), were worn by Bolan at a number of live concerts in 1972 and are highly collectable today.**

£3,000-4,000

▼ **Marc Bolan wore this candy-striped jacket in the film *Born To Boogie*, shot at the Empire Pool, Wembley on 18 March 1972. Because the jacket is linked to a particular star and event it will command a premium. Clothes not typical of Bolan's image are worth significantly less.**

£1,500-2,000

▲ **The American band Kiss were hugely popular in the 1970s with their mixture of glam-rock and heavy metal sound. The single *I Was Made For Loving You* reached 50 in the UK charts in 1979 and *Beth* reached number seven in the United States in 1976. Few Kiss items appear on the market outside the United States. These boots were part of the "super-hero"-style costumes worn by Kiss in their first film *Kiss Meets The Phantom* (1978) and are typical of their stage clothes. Each outfit has a silver and black body suit, platform boots and a wax mask head.**

£20,000+ the set

▼ Quite a number of articles of Stevie Nicks' clothing have appeared for sale in recent years because she has donated several items to charities. The right foot of this pair of boots has been signed by her with "much love". In tan imitation leather, the boots are the epitome of 1970s' fashion. They were worn by Nicks on her first tour with Fleetwood Mac in 1975. A jacket she wore for the same tour embroidered with her name on the front was also offered for sale at an auction in 1993.

£550-650

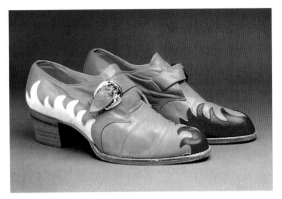

▲ Eric Clapton offered these shoes for sale at a raffle in the 1970s for Friends of the Earth. Because so little of his clothing appears on the market it is highly sought-after and the price will be correspondingly high. A Versace suit worn at the Albert Hall in 1991 was also donated by him to charity.

£1,000-1,500

► Freddie Mercury was another great stage performer who employed theatrical and dramatic effects during his performances. However, few of his costumes have appeared on the market. This particular suit was worn by him on stage in c.1979. It is accompanied by a machine-print photograph of him wearing the suit and this helps to establish its authenticity.

*Another costume belonging to Mercury that came up for sale recently was a chequerboard patterned leotard.

£3,000-4,000

◀▼ This unique Bob Dylan jacket is from his Born-Again Christian phase, after which he converted back to Judaism. It was given to Kinky Friedman, a member of his band, and is accompanied by a letter from him confirming its provenance.

£7,000-8,000

▼ When Elvis Presley's "Shooting Star" jumpsuit sold for £28,000 at auction in 1988 it broke the world record for a piece of rock and roll clothing. (This was later broken by Buddy Holly's glasses which sold for £30,000 in New York – see p. 81.) The suit was designed by Bill Belew who produced many designs for Elvis in a style now synonymous with the star. It was worn during a concert at Madison Square Gardens in 1972 and is one of his most famous outfits, appearing in films, books and magazines. Less well-known examples command lower prices.

▼ Far less of the clothing that John Lennon wore in the 1970s appears on the market than from his Beatles' years in the 1960s. This 1970's cap has been signed by Lennon and was given as a prize to a fan by an American radio station in 1975.

£2,200-2,500

£28,000+

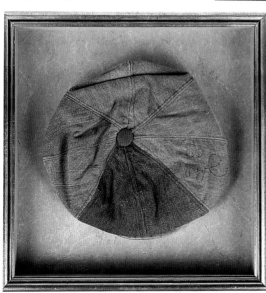

▶ A rather less collectable article of rock and roll clothing is this oyster satin tour jacket belonging to Jackie Jackson of The Jackson Five. If it was Michael Jackson's (he was also a member of the group), it would be far more collectable, but there is less interest in the rest of the band. Michael went solo in 1979 when he released his first album *Off The Wall*.

£400-600

▲ Elvis Presley was a keen devotee of karate – he received a black belt in 1960, qualifying to the 7th degree in 1974 – and he frequently incorporated karate moves into his performances. This custom made Gi/Doe Bouk karate suit is one of only three designed by Elvis and Master Rhee, his instructor. It was sold together with 31 photographs of Elvis. **£11,000+**

▼ This cape forms part of a similar outfit to the "Shooting Star" jumpsuit on the opposite page. Although highly decorative, the suit is far less famous and consequently it is worth considerably less. Elvis had a number of specially commissioned stage belts designed by Bill Belew and these have also appeared on the market in recent years.

£7,000-8,000

◀ Because this Western-style jacket is not that generally associated with Marc Bolan its value is far less than any of his glam-rock clothes. It was given to Bolan by Ringo Starr and is accompanied by a letter of authenticity from Bolan's former road manager.

£250-350

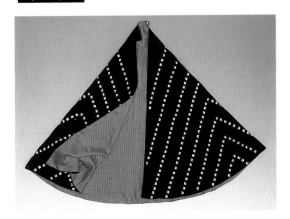

1980s – Michael Jackson

Michael Jackson was the most successful rock and pop performer of the 1980s, with his 1987-1988 *Bad* world tour making unprecedented sums. Despite the quantity of suits worn by Michael Jackson both on stage and off, relatively few appear on the market. A biker's style jacket with fringes was sold in the same year as the sequinned jacket featured on the right. A pair of boots with silver decoration on the heels and toes have also been offered for sale. Most desirable are those highly-distinctive items Jackson has been seen wearing on a concert tour or on the cover of an album. As with any major contemporary pop star, Jackson's clothing is likely to become far more collectable over the years when supply has become more limited.

▲ Michael Jackson wore these rhinestone shoes during the *Jackson Live* tour in 1981. He appears on the cover of the album of the same name wearing them, a factor which makes them instantly recognizable and highly sought-after. Michael Jackson gave the shoes to a friend as a present, with a note saying "This is memorabilia David, enjoy it", acknowledging the field of rock and roll memorabilia, and also showing the rise in status of this field of collecting in recent years.

£5,000-6,000

▶ At the time of his *Bad* concerts Michael Jackson had adopted the "bondage" look, harking back to the punk rock era of the 1970s. He wore this black leather suit extensively on stage throughout what was the highest grossing concert tour to date. Both garments bear the label Western Costume Co., Hollywood and Michael Jackson's name. **£18,000**

▼ Another trademark item of Michael Jackson's clothing but far less rare than his gloves is this fedora made by the Golden Gate Hat Company in Los Angeles. Jackson developed a habit of throwing these out to the audience during his concerts. Some of the hats are signed (on the brim where the signature can be seen) and have his name stamped inside somewhere – this example has Jackson's name in gold lettering.

£400-800

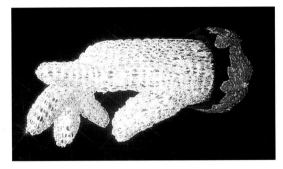

▼ Michael Jackson wore this typical sequinned and buckled jacket on tour and also for the famous cola commercial in 1984.

£8,000-10,000

▲ Michael Jackson is known for wearing one glove, which he said he felt to be "cool" and "definitely a look". This example was sold in London in 1991.

£16,500+

▼ This leather jacket was worn by Michael Jackson during the filming of the 1983 video *Thriller*, which proved to be a milestone in pop promotions.

£3,500-4,000

1980s – Madonna

Madonna's powerful stage image has largely been a heady mixture of sexual and religious imagery and nearly all the clothing associated with her is overtly sexy – red and black silk, bustiers, stockings and tassels are regular features. The increasingly dominant sexual aspect of her persona was confirmed by the best-selling book *Sex* (1992) which shocked many with its content.

▼ Of Italian descent, Madonna had a Catholic upbringing and many of the costumes she wore in the early days of her career incorporated religious motifs into them. She wore this crucifix necklace extensively on stage during her 1985 *Like A Virgin* tour and is featured in the concert programme wearing it.

£3,000-4,000

◀ The fact that Madonna has signed this pair of Italian black leather shoes immediately increases their value – the words "Express Yourself" are from one of her singles. She wore the shoes on her *Like A Virgin* tour and donated them to charity in the United States.

£1,400-1,600

▼ This black leather one-piece outfit is probably one of the very best pieces of clothing belonging to Madonna to appear on the market. It epitomizes her overtly sexual image and features in her book *Sex*. As with many of her clothes, Madonna has signed the costume and given it away to a friend, tacitly acknowledging the fact that her clothing will realize high prices when sold on the open market.

*Madonna has proved to be the most commercially successful female performer of recent times. Since her first success in 1984, when she released her single *Holiday*, she has adopted a variety of guises and developed a series of complex and highly theatrical stage shows which can be compared to those by Michael Jackson.

£4,000-6,000

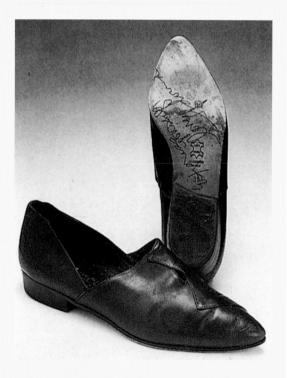

▼ This black satin bustier was worn by Madonna on her *Who's That Girl* tour in 1987, and the programme from the tour features pictures of her wearing it. The boned bodice is trimmed in gold and like many of her clothes, it has distinctive padded cups and tassels. It has been signed by her in gold felt tip pen and was given, like the crucifix on the left, to her choreographer on the tour, Brad Jeffries. Because bustiers are one of the items of clothing most associated with Madonna they are greatly sought-after and also expensive.

*A number of Madonna's Gaultier bustiers have also appeared on the market in recent years.

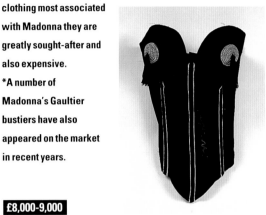

£8,000-9,000

▲ This pair of sheer nylon knickers have the word "kiss" in white felt and rhinestones on the back. They were worn by Madonna on the *Who's That Girl* tour in 1987 and also feature on the *Ciao Italia* video.

*Items of underwear belonging to sex symbols have always been desirable – a pair of stockings which were worn by Marilyn Monroe were sold at auction in 1993.

£1,200-1,500

► Madonna wore this baby-doll négligé during her *Blonde Ambition* world tour in 1990, and several publicity cards show her wearing the outfit on stage. A letter from her assistant Stephanie Stephens confirms its authenticity. As with other examples of clothing which have appeared at major rock and pop auctions, Madonna donated this négligé to charity. Such items are particularly popular for display in restaurants and other "theme" venues.

£10,000-12,000

1980s – Prince

Prince is well-known for his highly individual stage costumes. Purple is one of the colours most closely associated with him, following his *Purple Rain* Tour between 1984 and 1985. He has changed his image several times during his career and usually adopts an entirely different wardrobe for each tour he undertakes. Prince is particularly fond of colour co-ordinating his clothes and he frequently wears matching accessories – for example, shoes, lace gloves and handkerchiefs.

◀ Prince wore this iridescent purple lurex coat during the Grammy Awards ceremony in 1983 when he received an award for his album *1999*. The studded detail on the shoulders is very similar to the kind of decoration used to adorn Michael Jackson's clothes (see pp. 88-89). Like much celebrity clothing, this coat was donated by Prince as a prize to raise money for charity – in this case an event organized by Capital Radio in Los Angeles .

£4,000-5,000

▲ Prince usually makes several costume changes during a concert. This black polyester crêpe, ruff-fronted shirt was worn by him at a concert in Rotterdam on 19 August 1986. It was one of several shirts he wore at the concert that he subsequently threw out into the audience. Another item from this concert, a matador jacket, has also been offered for sale at a recent auction in London, along with a white shirt identical in style to this one.

£1,000-1,200

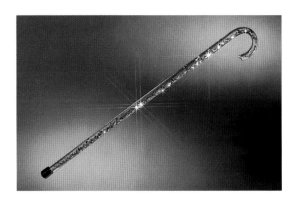

▲ This distinctive perspex cane filled with purple, blue, silver and gold glitter in the shape of hearts, circles and stars from Prince's *Purple Rain* tour emphasizes the impression of showmanship that he liked to convey during his performances.

£1,200-1,500

◀ This turquoise and black silk suit with an asymmetrical design is typical of those worn by Prince. This particular example was made specially for him by the wardrobe department at Paisely Park in the United States for his appearance at the 1988 Grammy Awards. Although of significant value, this may have been boosted further had it been pictured on one of his album covers, or worn extensively on tour. Nevertheless, it is a fine example of the sense of theatre he creates so strongly though his unique costumes.

£5,000-7,000

▼ The period of Prince's *Purple Rain* tour (1984-1985) was particularly notable for some of the fantastic costumes he wore during his shows. The high heels on this pair of boots are typical of those found on his shoes – Prince is very small, so he has to wear high heels to make him appear taller on stage. The boots are decorated in a colourful

psychedelic pattern and were made to match one of his outfits worn for the tour. They were offered for sale with Prince's autograph.

£2,500-3,000

▼ Like Michael Jackson's fedora hats, the hats worn by Prince were also a notable feature of his stage image. This particular example is very ordinary-looking but the fact that it was worn by Prince and is accompanied by a letter confirming its authenticity immediately gives it a value far exceeding its second-hand worth. His co-star in the *Purple Rain* film, Appolonia Kotero, was given the hat by Prince during filming.

*In the case of an item of clothing that has no ostensible feature which automatically links it to a particular performer such evidence concerning its provenance is crucial. Without this evidence, the hat would have virtually no value at all.

£500-600

1980s and 1990s – Others

Since the singular success of the Live Aid concert in 1985, rock and pop and charitable events have become inextricably linked. The sale of personal possessions and memorabilia has proved to be a highly effective way of raising money and often gives collectors the opportunity to acquire items which would otherwise never come on the market. As can be seen in this section, clothing is often donated by performers. Collectors place a premium on those items which were associated with a significant point in an artist's career.

◄ George Michael tends to wear everyday clothes on stage rather than costumes. However, this black leather biker's jacket, signed on the left sleeve and worn in the video *Faith* (1987) is very distinctive. Clothing worn in promotional videos is generally highly prized by collectors.

£3,000-4,000

▲ Elton John continued wearing flamboyant clothes until c.1986, after which he changed his image completely. This stage outfit designed by Bob Mackie in 1986 is one of his most elaborate. It is a great display item and would be eagerly bought by the many fans of Elton John (see pp. 82-83).

£5,000-6,000

▼ Items of clothing from more recently-successful bands appear on the market at regular intervals. Although not as collectable as possessions of a highly-important artist they will still have specialist appeal. This sequinned lycra suit was worn by Shiobhan Fahey of Shakespeare's Sister during the band's *Hormonally Yours* tour and also on the band's video for the single *Stay*, which was number one in the British charts in 1992 for eight weeks. Despite the band's relatively modest success the value of the jacket is surprisingly high (see below left).

► Tears For Fears donated these suits worn by them on the cover of their *Sowing The Seeds Of Love* album (1991) to raise money for charity. Designed by Jasper Conran, they have been "customized" by the additional decoration of spray paint. The suits would have been very expensive when they were initially bought because of their designer label and it is interesting that the price they fetched when sold at auction in 1992 seemed quite modest when compared with their initial cost. They were worn together with matching shirts and shoes.

£900-1,000

£450-500 the set

▲ A strong feature of Sinead O'Connor's image are her Dr Marten boots. Popularized by the "skinheads" of the 1970s, they re-emerged in the 1990s and are as much a feminist statement as a fashion accessory. Again, these boots were a charity donation. The fact that they are signed and well-worn will add to their value.

£600-700

▼ Annie Lennox has given a number of her possessions to charity. This pair of black lace-up boots, worn during Eurythmics' *Revenge* tour (1986-7) and for the "Free Nelson Mandela" concert in June 1988, have been signed by her on both soles in black felt tip pen. Other items of Lennox clothing to come on the market include a pair of red leather gloves in 1991.

£500-700

Musical Instruments

The electric guitar is at the very heart of rock and roll, so it is not surprising that guitars played by famous artists and guitars which have featured prominently in a significant live or studio performance now appear on the collectors' market for very high prices.

Guitars with no direct association with a well-known guitarist have to be exceptional in some way to command more than their second-hand value. Such examples are confined to vintage and classic instruments by the top manufacturers Fender and Gibson (see pp. 102-103). Many other guitars, which may be a good example of a certain design but which do not fit into the category of rock and pop memorabilia, are sold through specialist guitar magazines or through a second-hand guitar retailer rather than at auction.

Compared to other musical instruments guitars are easy to store and display – few collectors could house one full drum kit, let alone several. However, this does not mean that other instruments do not appear on the market. Some magnificent drum kits have been sold at auction over the years, played by such famous names as Keith Moon, Ginger Baker, Carl Palmer, Mitch Mitchell and John Bonham. A group of percussion instruments belonging to Keith Moon were the largest so far to be offered for sale – an amalgam of equipment used from around 1965 to 1975 comprising some 25 assorted drums, timpani and gongs, and many stands and accessories, it sold in London in August 1985 for a total of £5,280.

The purchase of pianos, organs and synthesizers involves similar logistical problems to the buying of drums, so they also have limited appeal. However, keyboards played by Elton John, Keith Emerson, Jon Lord, Paul McCartney, John Lennon, Pete Townshend and Cat Stevens have all been sold at auction in the past.

As with clothing, provenance and evidence that the instrument has been used are crucial to the value because the majority of instruments are of a standard design and there is nothing in their appearance which immediately associates them with a particular musician. The situation is helped if the instrument has been custom-built to an individual design. Theses include Prince's guitars, and some of Buddy Holly's, which are distinctive enough in their own right to be identified. Wherever possible it is advisable to obtain a statement from the musician whose instrument it was, stating when and where the item was purchased.

Condition is not crucial when buying a musical instrument and any normal wear and tear is perfectly acceptable. There are even some notable examples where damage (and even near-destruction) are highly desirable! The guitar-smashing antics of Jimi Hendrix and Pete Townshend are now so much a part of rock legend that their smashed guitars command a premium. In addition to those guitars shown in this section which have come on the market, are a Rickenbacker, broken during Pete Townshend's appearance on BBC television's *Top Of The Pops* in 1966, which sold for £3,300 in 1987, and an assortment of pieces from guitars he used in the 1960s sold in 1985 for £1,100.

Apart from the very high prices paid for those examples played by leading artists, there are a number of other musical instruments which can be bought for relatively low prices. The range is very varied, from mouth organs and tambourines, to a set of tubular bells, but although interesting to collect, the appearance on the market of such items is quite limited.

Left: A Gibson ES335 guitar, one of only 405 from 1960 with a Sunburst finish.
Above: Marc Bolan's Gibson Flying V guitar, 1964 Model, from c.1967/8.

Guitars

The electric guitar is at the basis of the whole rock and roll movement. In the United States the introduction of the Strastocaster model by Fender in 1954 coincided with Bill Haley's and Elvis Presley's progression from earlier country music to the guitar and drums-led rock and roll. It is not surprising therefore that guitars form an important part of any rock and roll auction sale. The most desirable are those used on significant recordings, and those owned by the most important stars – a guitar owned by John Lennon is highly-sought after because of his status as a musician. However, the highest prices are paid for an instrument owned and played by a guitar legend – Jimi Hendrix's guitars in particular fetch very high prices. Condition is often irrelevant because wear suggests use – Jimi Hendrix's smashed guitars command a premium. More than one guitar belonging to a particular star very rarely comes up for sale simultaneously. The exceptions are those of John Entwistle of The Who who sold more than 12 at auction in 1988, and Steve Howe of Yes who sold several from his extensive collection in 1987.

Collecting

Guitars are usually given by the artist to a friend or fellow-musician or are sold directly to a guitar shop to be sold second-hand. In all cases it is essential to have proof of provenance; anything "supposedly" or "allegedly" belonging to an artist will not sell.

▼ This semi-acoustic "Premier" Gibson guitar was used by Bill Haley in the late 1940s and early 1950s whilst as a rockabilly player he was developing the sound which is now known as rock and roll. The term itself is thought to have been coined by the American disc jockey, Alan Freed.

£15,000

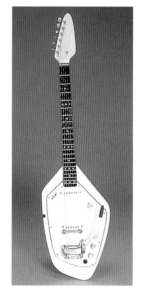

▲ The custom tooled leather cover made by Buddy Holly for his J45 acoustic guitar adds to its value considerably. **£150,000**

► The British guitar and amplifier manufacturer Vox pioneered this guitar organ in 1966. It was not a commercial success and it is likely that this example was presented to John Lennon as a gift but he was never pictured playing it.

£10,000

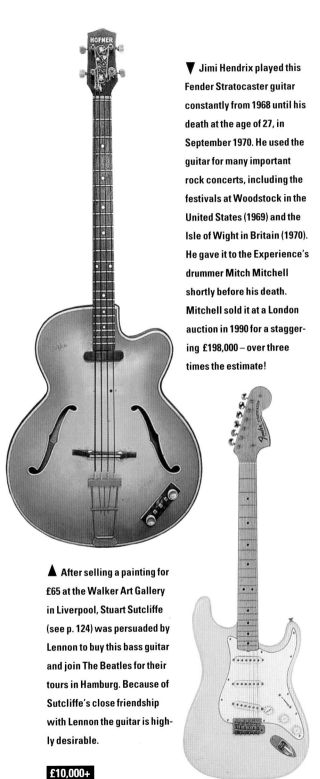

▼ Jimi Hendrix played this Fender Stratocaster guitar constantly from 1968 until his death at the age of 27, in September 1970. He used the guitar for many important rock concerts, including the festivals at Woodstock in the United States (1969) and the Isle of Wight in Britain (1970). He gave it to the Experience's drummer Mitch Mitchell shortly before his death. Mitchell sold it at a London auction in 1990 for a staggering £198,000 – over three times the estimate!

▲ After selling a painting for £65 at the Walker Art Gallery in Liverpool, Stuart Sutcliffe (see p. 124) was persuaded by Lennon to buy this bass guitar and join The Beatles for their tours in Hamburg. Because of Sutcliffe's close friendship with Lennon the guitar is highly desirable.

£10,000+

▼ ▶ Despite Jimi Hendrix's reputation for smashing his guitars on stage he actually did this quite infrequently and would often repair them to play again. Remnants are thus very rare and highly sought-after and

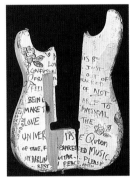

any "complete" sets such as these two sections which make up his customized Fender Stratocaster are almost non-existent. This item is made even more desirable by the addition of the poem written by Hendrix on the back, which expresses his love of his guitar. Photographs show Hendrix playing a similarly-decorated guitar at the Monterey Festival in the United States, and the guitar also appears in a photograph taken by an amateur (see p. 123) which was offered for sale at auction recently. The guitar sold for £30,000 in 1991 – over five times the estimate.

JIMI HENDRIX

Although Jimi Hendrix had a short career at the top in rock and roll (1966-1970) he is seen as probably the greatest electric guitar virtuoso of all time and his style and music have been emulated by many artists since. He was an excellent performer with an immediately distinctive style. He wore flamboyant clothes (see pp. 78-79), and being left-handed, played right-handed guitars upside down. His favoured instrument was the Fender Stratocaster, which in itself is a keystone of the rock and roll sound.

▼ In the early 1970s the Venolo Instrument Company produced a limited number of these experimental customized aluminium guitars. This one was owned by Marc Bolan and his name is printed below the tail piece. Although it is not the guitar immediately associated with Bolan, there are photographs of him playing it at concerts. Bolan is said to have given two other examples he had to Eric Clapton and Jeff Lynne (of ELO).

£6,000+ .

◀ Pete Townshend donated the remains of this Guild acoustic guitar to charity in 1989 and provided a letter confirming its authenticity which said "I broke it in frustration … I am not very proud of this."

£5,500+

▲ Noel Redding played this unusual eight-string Hagstrom bass guitar in 1967 on the Jimi Hendrix Experience's second album *Axis, Bold As Love,* and also at concerts – a photograph shows him using the guitar at the Ahoy Hallen, Rotterdam on 10 November 1967.

£8,000+

▶ Although Roy Orbison is not known as a guitarist, because of his status in the pop world this Gibson ES335 owned by him is still highly collectable. It was apparently used by Orbison during his recording sessions at Dave Stewart's house in Los Angeles as one of the Traveling Wilburys. This was a "Supergroup" set up in the late 1980s purely to produce records and whose members included Bob Dylan, George Harrison, Jeff Lynne and Tom Petty.

£4,500-5,000

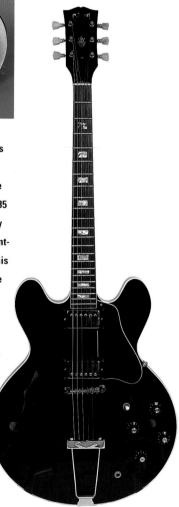

▶ Although Elvis Presley is not immediately thought of as a guitarist, his Martin D18 guitar sold for £99,000 at auction in May 1993 because it is from such a pivotal moment in his career. It was used for all his important Sun recordings and concerts between 1954 and 1956, and was sold by him to a music shop when he changed to the RCA label in September 1956. Documents sold with the guitar confirm its provenance.

◀ Performing as Derek And The Dominos, Eric Clapton and Duane Allman used this Martin D35 acoustic guitar during their recording sessions in Miami, most notably for *Layla* (1970). The fact that the guitar comes in its case with the band's name on it adds to its value, as does the fact that it was sold by the keyboard player of the band, Bobby Whitlock.

£7,000-8,000

SIGNERS

Another type of guitar which is becoming popular with collectors today is the "signer" – an ordinary guitar which has been signed by an artist who usually uses the particular make of guitar in hand. At other times the guitar is signed by a non-guitarist in the way that anything else is signed (such as record sleeves). Signers are of significantly less value than any guitar actually played and owned by a star, but provide a more affordable alternative.

101

▼ This 1960 Gibson Les Paul Standard guitar set a world record for a non-associated guitar when it sold for £18,700 in 1993. Less than two thousand examples were produced between 1958 and 1960 with a unique grained maple "flame-top". Today those with the most defined graining fetch the highest prices. This particular example has a good grain, is in excellent condition and had had one owner since 1966 who provided the original receipt from Burns Retail Ltd (where he bought the guitar) dated 22.8.66.

£18,700

▲ Prince's "Cloud" guitar is the one most closely associated with the star. This customized example was designed in 1983 by Prince's local guitar shop Knut Koupée for his appearance in the *Purple Rain* film. Prince is particularly known for his colour co-ordinated costumes (see pp. 92-93), and his guitars are often made to match. He gave this guitar to a New York radio station for presentation as a prize in a promotion competition and it is accompanied by a letter of provenance from his production company, Paisley Park.

£12,000

▼ This unique guitar in the shape of Africa was built to raise money for Sight Savers, the Royal Commonwealth Society For The Blind's appeal to raise money to fight river blindness in West Africa. It has been signed by a large number of stars including Stevie Wonder, Mark Knopfler, Eric Clapton, Pete Townshend, Sting and Bon Jovi and demonstrates the trend since Live Aid for charities to use rock and pop as a means to raise money.

£3,000+

◀ Fender was established in the United States in 1946 by Leo Fender and the first Stratocasters were made in 1954. Although this is one of the first made it is the non-tremolo version, worth only half as much as the tremolo version. Condition is crucial with vintage models, although signs of ageing and marks to the fret board are acceptable.

£3,500-4,500

▶ Because Jimmy Page who signed this guitar was formerly a guitarist with the rock band Led Zeppelin, and because the guitar is the make that is normally associated with him – a Gibson Les Paul Standard – it is worth far more than its second-hand value, but substantially less than had Page owned it himself. The inscription *"Keep on 'rockin'"* on the scratch plate is a typical Page expression.

£1,500-1,800

THE FENDER STRATOCASTER AND THE GIBSON LES PAUL

These two classic guitar designs form the backbone of rock and roll. More artists have played them than any other types. Early examples made in the 1950s before mass-production techniques were mastered are the most collectable and are very rare today. Later ones are far less expensive and are readily available in second-hand shops. The sound of the two guitars is quite different. The Stratocaster produces a brighter, more jangly sound than the richer, heavier tones of the Les Paul, which is favoured by blues and heavy metal guitar players.

▶ This Spanish classical acoustic guitar is a "signer". This one was signed by Bob Dylan and dated 10.2.86. It comes with a photograph which shows the original owner with Dylan holding the guitar just after the event. Because Dylan's signature is rare the guitar is still worth between £700 and £900, even though it has no direct association with the star – if it had been played by him it would be worth thousands of pounds.

£700-900

Straps and Tambourines

▼ This studded leather guitar strap has a double premium as it was owned and used by John Lennon and then given to Eric Clapton whilst he was playing with Cream in c.1966/7. The existence of photographs and a poster showing John Lennon wearing the strap will add to its desirablity because they confirm its use by a star.

£3,000

Guitar Straps

Guitar straps very rarely appear for sale and tend to be of little value unless they are associated with a particularly famous star – only Jimi Hendrix's appear in quantity. Straps are usually quite distinctive and like a star's clothes reflect the taste of the person wearing them. Provenance is very important as there is little visual evidence on the straps to show ownership.

Tambourines

Tambourines are the most disposable and inexpensive musical instruments played by rock and roll stars. They are frequently thrown out into the audience and retrieved by a fan to be signed by the artist. There is very seldom any association value as few people are known as tambourine players. They are of no great value as an object and are more like souvenirs – signed examples are the most desirable.

▼ This tambourine which has been signed and inscribed on the skin with the words "Love Marc Bolan xx" will be much sought-after by collectors. The signature was probably obtained by a fan after a T. Rex concert.

£350-400

▼ One of the few artists particularly associated with playing the tambourine is Stevie Nicks of Fleetwood Mac. She has inscribed this

example with the lines "You are the poet in my heart" taken from the band's hit single *Sara*. It was used by Nicks during the *Tusk* world tour in 1979 and comes with a backstage pass and unused ticket for the concert at Wembley.

£400-450

▶ This American Indian beaded strap is distinctive and was owned by Paul Kossoff, lead guitarist with Free. The band released their debut album *Tons Of Sobs* in 1969 and by the time of their third album *Fire And Water* (1970) they had achieved considerable success, and their hit single *All Right Now* was a massive world-wide hit. The strap was sold in 1993 by Kossoff's father to raise money for charity.

£250

▼ It is unlikely that this tambourine has ever been used. Signed by the rapper MC Hammer, it has been printed with the words, "2 Legit 2 Quit", and was designed to promote the album of that name. Because MC Hammer currently appeals to a small section of the collector's market the

value is significantly lower than if it the tambourine were associated with a longer established name. Compare the low price with the value of Stevie Nick's tambourine opposite.

£40-50

▼ Buddy Holly made this leather guitar strap in c.1955 to match his Gibson guitar (see p. 98). Although highly collectable, if it had been sold with the guitar its value may have increased substantially.

£5,000-6,000

◀ Bill Haley is seen wearing this tooled leather strap bearing his name and decorated with floral patterns on the front of the programme for Bill Haley and the Comets' British tour between March and April 1979 which assures its provenance and places it in a historical context. It was given to Jerry Tilley, lead guitarist with the Comets (1976-1981) and is inscribed "To Jerry – a pleasure working with you pal, Bill Haley".

£800-1,200

Pianos and Microphones

Pianos

Certainly, there are fewer rock and roll stars whose first instrument is the piano, rather than the guitar, and Elton John is probably the most famous of these. Pianos infrequently appear on the market because stars would usually use the instrument provided by the studio or would hire one for a concert. Stars often had pianos at home which they used to compose songs on – John Lennon used to own a number, and several have appeared on the market in recent years. Pianos are rare and expensive compared to other instruments, very few are bought to play, and they really only appeal to very dedicated collectors.

Microphones

Microphones tend to be sold by various recording studios as second-hand items. Only those which have been owned by a famous star or used on a successful recording are collectable today.

▼ Although John Lennon's Broadwood upright piano is basically an ordinary instrument it was used by Lennon to compose four important songs for The Beatles' *Sergeant Pepper* album and is therefore highly collectable. On the side of the piano is a brass plaque which states that "On this piano was written: A Day in the Life, Lucy in the Sky with Diamonds, Good Morning, Good Morning and Being for the Benefit of Mr Kite and many others". It is also accompanied by a letter which confirms its authenticity.

£12,000-15,000

▲ Although there is no visible evidence that this microphone was used by The Beatles it is still a highly valuable item because it was installed in the Casbah Coffee Club, Liverpool, and used in the early 1960s when The Beatles were performing there at the beginning of their career. Its provenance is assured because it was sold by The Beatles' drummer, Pete Best, in whose mother's basement the club was located.

£3,500-4,000

▼ The brightly-painted decoration on Elton John's upright piano from the 1960s is characteristic of the period and is a hint of his later flamboyance (also reflected in the numerous extravagant outfits he had specially designed for his stage performances – see pp. 82-83). Elton John used this piano to compose songs before he was famous, and there is no visual record of him having played it at any concerts.

*A number of other Elton John pianos have come up for sale, including a baby grand in 1985.

£3,000-3,500

▶ This Bechstein grand piano was hired from the London music shop Samuels and used as the resident piano at the Trident Studios in the 1960s and 1970s. It was used by many influential artists on a number of highly successful recordings, including among others Queen, The Beatles on their *White Album*, David Bowie on *Space Oddity*, *Hunky Dory* and *Ziggy Stardust*, and Elton John on *Goodbye Yellow Brick Road*, *Blue Moves* and *A Single Man*. Not only is it an important instrument in the history of popular music, it is also valuable in its own right as a piano.

£15,000-18,000

▼ This is one of the only examples of a personally-owned microphone to be offered for sale. A recording microphone, it was used by Buddy Holly to compose songs at home in c.1957.

£1,000-1,500

▲ When Paul McCartney's Chappell and Co. upright piano, played by him as a teenager, was offered for sale at a London auction in 1981 it triggered the whole phenomenon of rock and pop auction sales in the United Kingdom.

£10,000-15,000

Drum Kits and Skins

There are only a handful of rock and roll artists who are famous as drummers, and it tends to be the instruments of these few that appear for sale. Apart from The Beatles' drummer, Ringo Starr, the most collectable drums are those of The Who's drummer, Keith Moon. He played the drums in the same way as he lived his life, and is famous for smashing up his drum kits on stage. Complete drum kits are quite rare and have a limited appeal as they are so large – drum skins are far easier to collect. The donation of signed drumskins is an increasingly popular way for stars, such as Phil Collins, to help raise money for charity.

▲ Keith Moon's drum kits are usually very impressive and many were custom-built. He wanted this 13-piece set to have gold-fittings, but on the advice of the makers, Premier, he settled for copper which was far more durable for the treatment the drums would receiye! Such a large and extensive set is very rare and is highly collectable despite the logistics of storage.

£7,000-9,000

◀ One of the most unusual sets to appear for sale is this complete set of stage equipment used by U2 in the recording studio and on stage, mainly during the production of the feature film *Rattle And Hum*. Not only is it a whole set, each piece has been clearly signed by the respective member of the band, suggesting it was probably originally sold to raise money for charity. When it was offered for sale at a London auction in 1989 it sold for £11,000.

£11,000

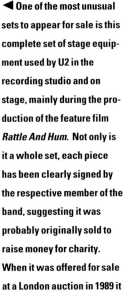

▲ Only three or four of Ringo Starr's drum skins with The Beatles' logo were made and consequently they are some of the most sought-after. Provenance is of the utmost importance as the skins are easy to fake and dubious ones do come on the market.

£11,500-13,000

▶ If this five-piece part drum set had not been fitted with this particular skin it would probably be worth only half the price. The skin was originally designed by Premier for a kit for Keith Moon in 1967 to promote the single *Pictures Of Lily*. The logo has been so widely seen that it has almost become their trademark. The skin was taken off the original drum and put on this bass drum a year later. It has been used for playing, which has left pedal-wear to the centre of the design.

£8,000

▶ John Bonham's fast and furious drum playing was a key element of Led Zeppelin's distinctive sound. This Ludwig drum kit was donated by Bonham to raise money for a local home for mentally handicapped children in 1978. It was used extensively on the band's tour in the United States. See-through perspex drums were popular only for a short time because they were not very durable and did not produce a good sound. A similar drum set with orange and yellow candy stripes played by Cream's Ginger Baker was offered for sale in 1985.

£4,000

▼ The Jam's drummer, Rick Buckler, has not only signed this snare drum and listed the names of various songs he used the drum for, but has also written a letter confirming the drum's authenticity, beginning "This snare I used extensively on tour and in the studio...". The Jam were one of the most successful post-punk bands, producing four number one hits in five years.

£400-500

▼ Cream was a collaboration of three outstanding musicians whose career was short but highly influential. The drummer, Ginger Baker, displayed outstanding expertise and his drums are keenly sought-after. This skin from 1966 is reputedly painted by Baker himself. Condition is crucial for items bought to display.

£1,500-2,000

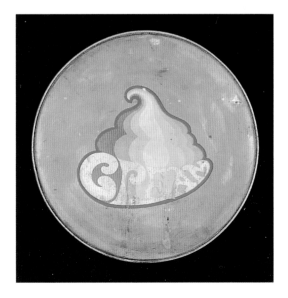

Other Instruments & Equipment

A wide variety of musical instruments and equipment come up for sale which are interesting because of their association with a particular artist. Those instruments that feature on an important or successful recording command the highest prices because they are fundamental in producing a famous sound. Such items are sought after, not only by collectors of rock and roll, but also by musicians who buy the equipment to use. Recording equipment in particular tends to have rather an esoteric appeal, and is most likely to be bought by an avid collector of one artist or band. Much equipment is sold as second-hand material in music shops. If there is no obvious distinguishing feature there needs to be something which ties the instrument to the artist to make it collectable.

▶ Fuzz boxes – foot pedals used with a guitar to distort the sound – were popular in the 1960s when musicians were keen to experiment with sound effects. This example was used by Jimi Hendrix, one of its first exponents, and was sold together with one of his bandannas and a letter from his father offering the original vendor "First chose (sic) of the head bands ...."

£650-700

▼ There is no firm evidence that John Lennon used this Hohner harmonica in the recording studio but because it was owned by him it is still very valuable. It was sold by his former housekeeper at Kenwood.

£2,200-2,600

◀ Stevie Wonder donated this Hohner harmonica to a charity auction at the Paramount Studios in Hollywood. Because it is the instrument most closely associated with Wonder its value is substantial.

£650-750

▼ This is one of three designs of juke box produced by the Seeburg company, all of which are of a similar shape which has become known as the "trash can" or "washing machine". This example, model 147, plays 20 selections of 78 rpm discs. The whole lid opens out to load and unload the discs. The fact that the mechanism is hidden inside the juke box meant it was not a commercial success at the time that it was made because people liked to see the workings of the machine. However, because there were far fewer of this type of juke box made than of the Wurlitzer above, examples are greatly sought-after and command high prices today.

£4,000-5,000

▲ Wurlitzer is the most famous make of juke box – the other three are AMI (Automatic Music Instrument Company), Seeburg and Rock-Ola. This Wurlitzer 1015 is the classic juke box design and incorporates many typical elements, including a bubble light tube which changes colour as the music plays. It was advertized in an uprecedented campaign in the United States. The model, which plays 24 selections of 78rpm records, was introduced in 1946 by Paul Fuller who designed most of Wurlitzer's classics. This box is in good condition and the mechanism – which is totally visible – is in good mechanical order. Sometimes the original 78rpm records are included, but although desirable, these are not essential.

£4,500-6,000

JUKE BOXES

Juke boxes originated in the United States late in the 1920s and spread to the rest of the world together with rock and roll later on in the 1950s. They were particularly popular in the United States during the Second World War when they were installed in thousands of diners, cafés and bars. Juke boxes from the early days are the most elaborate and inter-esting in design, many adopt-ing typical Art Deco motifs; those from the 1950s and 1960s are squarer and less innovative. The early models are the most sought after and command the highest prices, and are the only boxes to appear for sale at major auc-tions – later models are usual-ly sold in specialist shops. It is more important for the machine to be as close as pos-sible to its original form than to be in good working order. With many the internal mechanisms have been totally replaced. Any that have been altered to play 45rpm records are sub-stantially devalued. Juke boxes are often bought for dis-play in cafés and bars but a large number are bought by collectors who are attracted by the boxes' strong visual appeal.

◄ The Mellotron, developed by a West Midland company as a predecessor to the synthesiser, plays pre-taped recordings of music or voices which are activated by hitting a particular key. They were very popular in the late 1960s when musicians were experimenting with sound as part of the psychedelic movement (see pp. 118-121). This Mellotron belonged to John Lennon and was used on the track *Bungalow Bill* from the *White Album* – the music is still stored in the machine so the fact that there is no written provenance makes little difference. A Mellotron was also used for the recording of *Strawberry Fields*.

£8,000-10,000

► Jon Lord is one of the best-known keyboard players in rock and roll. He played with Deep Purple and then Whitesnake, two of the most successful and influential heavy rock bands of the 1970s. This Minimoog synthesizer was used extensively by Lord in the 1970s and comes with a letter of authenticity from him confirming its use.

£800-1,200

► As with the violin on the opposite page this Piccolo (Octave) trumpet is important because it was played on the Beatles' tracks, *Penny Lane*, recorded at the Abbey Road studio on 17 January 1967, and *All You Need Is Love*, recorded on 25 June 1967. Paul McCartney heard classical musician David Mason playing it in a performance of the Brandenburg Concerto and asked him to play on *Penny Lane*. Mason's contribution was inspired. It was he who sold the instrument in 1987.

£7,000-8,000

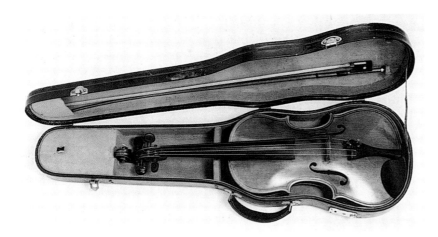

▼ This Beatles' Fender "Pro-Amp" amplifier was of the type used by the band between 1968 and 1969.

£500-700

▲ This violin was played in the country music solo on the track *Don't Pass Me By* from The Beatles' *White Album* (1968). It was sold by Jack Fallon, the session musician who played it on the track, together with the payment invoice for the session, £11.

£1,800-2,000

► This PA system used by The Sex Pistols is large and of limited appeal. It was bought from The Pistols' drummer Paul Cook in 1981 by The Anti-Nowhere League. The battered condition evokes the punk image, and the 500 watt capacity reflects the small venues in which the bands played.

£150-200

▼ This Selmer tenor saxophone features on Pink Floyd's album *Dark Side Of The Moon* (1973), on the track *Money*. It was sold by the musician who played it on tour with the band, complete with its original case covered in stickers which add further historical interest.

£1,000-1,200

Miscellaneous

Apart from the items featured in this book which fit into the major areas of rock and roll collectables, there is a rich diversity of other material related to pop stars which caters for all pockets and all tastes.

The market is dominated by Beatles-related memorabilia, which has been sold at every price level and constitutes a wide range of objects. The most expensive example is John Lennon's highly distinctive customized Rolls-Royce, which sold in 1985 for over two million dollars – the highest price paid for a piece of rock and pop memorabilia to date. The price was probably realized not only because of Lennon's huge following, but also because the car is a striking period piece which captures an important moment in rock history. It mixes the flower power mood of 1967 (when

The Beatles released the landmark album *Sergeant Pepper* album) with the characteristic Lennon notion of taking one of the most potent symbols of wealth and status and painting it with a design more commonly found on a barge or gypsy caravan!

Few other names in rock and roll have The Beatles' power to make even the most unremarkable personal possessions highly collectable. This is admirably illustrated by the inclusion in a sale at a London auction in 1990 of a white fibreglass, circular bath removed from Lennon's former home of Tittenhurst Park, which although ostensibly just an ordinary bath, sold for £715.

Among the least expensive rock and pop memorabilia is the vast range of Beatles-related merchandise produced in Britain and the United States to cash in on the tidal wave of Beatlemania sweeping the two countries in the early 1960s. No other rock and pop star or band had previously had such an effect and very few have inspired such a phenomenon. Because some of The Beatles' most dedicated fans were teenage girls, many of the products were designed specifically for them – for example, clothing and make-up. So ingenious were the manufacturers that it was possible for the keen fan to have The Beatles' images on each item of furnishing in every room, and on hundreds of objects used in a normal day, both at home and school. When The Beatles' released their cartoon, *Yellow Submarine*, in 1968, it launched a second batch of Beatles-related memorabilia, which has never been matched since.

Another inexpensive area of collecting not covered elsewhere in this book is that of posters, programmes and other unsigned promotional material. Although concert posters from the 1960s featuring the biggest names have now become very valuable, there is a wealth of other promotional material from the 1970s and later which is far more affordable. Collectors should always choose examples in the best condition they can afford because unless the item is so rare that this is not really a consideration it will help it to maintain its value in the future.

Most of the memorabilia in this section was produced inexpensively at the time, and is widely available today at affordable prices. It is an ideal place to start a collection, particularly for those on a limited budget because a fascinating collection can be built up in a relatively short period of time. Items in this category are most usually offered for sale at record fairs and through personal advertisements in specialist magazines rather than at auction. Although this is a relatively new area within collecting, rock and pop-related merchandise is as mixed and varied as the music and artists that have inspired it, and it provides one of the most interesting and colourful collecting areas for any rock and pop enthusiast.

Left: Four miniature Beatles "nodding head" dolls mounted on a cardboard stage.

Above: A limited edition Eta watch, decorated with a portrait of David Bowie and his facsimile signature.

Personal Possessions

Such is the status of some rock and roll stars that anything owned by him or her, even household and everyday objects, becomes immediately valuable and desirable. Personal possessions that come on to the collector's market include private documents such as birth certificates, furnishings and furniture, and – most regularly and most popular with collectors today – cars. When collecting personal possessions, provenance is crucial as a prospective buyer needs written or visual proof that the item they are buying was definitely owned by the star – without this the item is merely of second-hand value.

▼ John Lennon's customized Rolls-Royce Phantom V touring limousine broke the world record when it sold for $2,299,000 at auction in New York in 1985 (ten times its estimate). The car was bought by Lennon in 1966 and was painted by a friend who decorated it with a typical psychedelic design (see p.120-121). The car was used by The Beatles between 1966 and 1969 then loaned to other groups of the time before being sold to the United States in 1970 and consequently donated to the Cooper-Hewitt Museum in 1977. It is difficult to imagine any other single item associated with a rock star that could possibly beat this unprecedented price.

▲ TWA issued special flight bags to The Beatles printed with "The Beatles to the USA August 1965, TWA" on one side for their trip to the United States in August 1965. The flight bags, made for the four members of the band, were printed with their name on the other side, but those given out to their entourage were not named in this way. The airline quickly grasped the news of the band being awarded their MBEs on 12 June of that year and has added the letters of the award after each name on the front of the bag. *Other examples of this TWA travel bag without a printed name on have come up for sale at auction (for example, one belonging to Mal Evans) and these are worth between £700-800, whereas this one produced for Paul McCartney is worth considerably more.

£1,000-1,500

▼ Even items utterly removed from a star's musical activites can be sought after, as shown by this globe cocktail cabinet which was bought by John Lennon from Aspreys in London and used at his house, Kenwood, in the 1960s. Its provenance is secured because it was sold by his wife, Cynthia. It is a typical sixties item which will appeal to collectors of The Beatles.

£1,000+

▲ Cars fetch prices far above their second-hand value if they were once the possession of a famous rock and roll star. This 1977 Panther de Ville Coupé was owned by Elton John and his name appears on the engine plate. The car appeared in the video to promote his single *I'm Still Standing* in 1983 and sold at auction in London in 1991 for £46,200.

▶ This copy of John Lennon's birth certificate was issued in August 1960, four days before The Beatles made their very first trip to Hamburg.

£2,000+

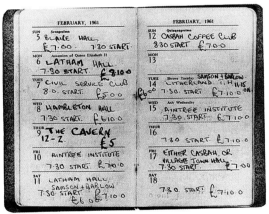

▲ Although this is an ordinary pocket diary, because it was the property of The Beatles' first drummer, Pete Best, it is an extremely important collector's item. It gives a detailed record of The Beatles' bookings for the year 1961, with a list of venues, starting-times and fees, as well as some important numbers at the back, including that of the Cavern Club. It is interesting that the fee for their first Cavern Club booking on 9 February was £5, but by July of the same year it had risen to £15. The provenance of the diary is clear because it was sold by Pete Best himself.

£3,000-4,000

Psychedelia

The term psychedelia is derived from the word psychedelic meaning "expanding the mind's awareness". It refers to a particular movement that blossomed in the United States in 1966 and spread to the United Kingdom a year later. The movement emerged with music developed on the West Coast of the United States and not only permeated that music and art but also embodied a whole philosophy which is synonymous with the "flower power" movement and feelings of "free love". Much of the artwork and music was apparently inspired by hallucinatory drugs such as LSD; direct reference was supposedly made to this influence in The Beatles' track, *Lucy In The Sky With Diamonds*. In Britain, The Beatles were a leading exponent of psychedelia, but The Rolling Stones also followed some of the philosophy. In the United States bands such as Jefferson Airplane, Quicksilver Messenger Service, The Grateful Dead and Love are closely associated with psychedelia. The artwork is usually in exceptionally bright or fluorescent colours, sometimes with "metallic" finishes and writing which may not be immediately legible. Much psychedelia that comes on the market today consists of rock and pop posters, mainly from the United States.

▼ Original psychedelic artwork is rare. This example (21½ x 14in, 54 x 36cm) for the Jimi Hendrix Experience has been signed by the artist, David Ward Byrd, who also produced the original poster for the Woodstock Festival when it was scheduled to be held in Wallkill, New York.

£2,000

▲ The decoration on this Spanish acoustic guitar was inspired by the band Cream who were formed in 1966. Although not directly associated with a rock star it is still a fun item and evocative of the period.

£300-400

► This original poster design for the UK magazine *Valentine* is by the German artist Helmut Klein. He also produced designs for *Yellow Submarine* and stylistic similarities between them are obvious.

£350-450

▼ A classic piece of psychedelic imagery, this poster of Bob Dylan by Martin Sharp, 1967, makes use of lyrics and song titles within a colourful and eyecatching design. Its innovative "metallic" finish, makes it one of the best examples of 1960s English poster artwork. Other well known psychedelic artists include Steffan Hope, Alan Aldridge, Rick Griffin, Gunther Keiser, Val Wilmer and Roger Dean.

£100-200

► Psychedelic posters produced for English events rarely appear on the market. This example echoes exactly the style of American ones, with typical graphics and bright colours. It is advertising a "14 Hour Technicolour Dream" held at the Alexandra Palace in London in April 1967. All-night music events were a new phenomenon at this time, featuring many bands and fantastic light shows, and became extremely popular.

£300-400

► One of the most unusual psychedelic items to appear on the market is this refrigerator made by Philips in Italy in 1967, known as the *General's Wardrobe*. Only 500 were made available in the United Kingdom, originally for shop display purposes only. However, due to continued requests

to buy them a retail price of £73.12s.5d was set. Although this refrigerator is in good working order this will not greatly affect the price.

£700-800

◀ Bill Graham promoted many rock and roll concerts at his famous East and West Coast venues in the United States throughout the 1960s. Posters produced for the concerts are now highly collectable. All the designs have been allocated a catalogue number and together they are known as the BG numbered series which comprises almost 300 designs. The posters infrequently appear on the market in the United Kingdom, and the estimate quoted below is based on values in the United States. This particular poster was produced for Six Days of Sound, a musical event held in aid of CND (Campaign for Nuclear Disarmament), a peace movement which was very strong in the 1960s.

*The poster was designed by Bonnie McLean who was married to Bill Graham.

£80-120

▶ By the time of the psychedelic movement decorative posters featuring pop stars were becoming very popular and could be seen adorning the walls of many teenagers' bedrooms. The posters were mass-produced and sold inexpensively through retail outlets and because of this only examples in pristine condition will have any collectable value; concert posters are always more popular.

*Any Jimi Hendrix material is highly sought-after; this decorative poster has a good image of the star and is in excellent condition so its value is relatively high.

£100-150

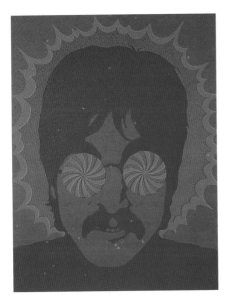

◀ The Apple shop in Baker Street, London, sold a whole series of Beatles-related posters in 1968 which would have only cost a few shillings to buy at the time. They were designed by The Fool (see right) and although some of the designs appear quite regularly at auction (for example, one entitled *A Is For Apple*), this psychedelic portrait of John Lennon is rare. The Fool also painted a massive psychedelic mural on the outside wall of the Apple shop which unfortunately no longer exists. The fact that this example is in particularly good condition will add to its value.

£50-70

▶ Big O Posters published a series of seven posters for The Beatles' songs in 1967. This example was designed by Martin Sharp – one of the most renowned designers of psychedelic art – for the single, *All You Need Is Love*. The poster is more collectable because it is one of a limited edition of only ten. Produced in silk screen on acetate, it is in typically bright colours of red and yellow.
*Unlike most original poster artwork, this example has been signed by the artist.

£300-500

COLLECTING PSYCHEDELIA

Prominent psychedelic artists in the Unites States were Peter Max (who designed psychedelic furniture and cushions), Rick Griffin and Stanley Mouse, and in the United Kingdom Martin Sharp, and Nigel Weymouth and Michael English (known as Hapshash and The Coloured Coat). Three Dutch artists, Simon Posthuma, Josje Leeger and Marijke Koger, set up a design team called The Fool which produced designs for The Beatles. Psychedelic art is particularly popular with collectors interested in the 1960s because it embodies the rock and roll culture of the time and has great visual appeal. As it was mass-produced, it is widely available at low prices today. Condition is therefore crucial; pin holes and folds are acceptable but tears can make a picture worthless. Many posters have been reprinted in recent years and these are of little value so it is important to confirm that any purchases are 1960s' originals; those produced by Hapshash and The Coloured Coat were all sillkscreen printed and generally have the same measurements (20 x 30in, 51 x 7cm).

Photographs

Photographic images of rock and roll pop stars fall into two categories; those taken by professionals at special sessions, and those taken by amateurs and fans at chance meetings. Some professional images, such as those by the photographer Gered Mankowitz, are very famous and highly sought-after, but amateur pictures can be just as valuable in providing a record of a star in relaxed moments. Copyright originally belongs to the photographer, but if, for example, an image has been used on an album cover, it may belong to the record company who purchased it. Photographs are sold both with and without copyright; those with copyright are far more valuable as they provide the opportunity to reproduce the image. Images never before published are particularly desirable, as are early photographs of The Beatles, and any of Jimi Hendrix.

▲ Gered Mankowitz has photographed many rock and roll stars including The Rolling Stones and Jimi Hendrix. His photographs have frequently been reproduced and many of the images are familiar. This portrait of The Rolling Stones entitled *Caged – 1965* is a recent print from the original negative and has been signed and annotated by Mankowitz in black ink on the border.
*This is a particularly well-known image as it was used on the cover of The Rolling Stones' Autumn 1965 tour programme.

£500

◀ When a make-up girl took this photograph of Jimi Hendrix at the Saville Theatre, London, in 1967, she unwittingly provided the only record of him holding the guitar which sold at a London auction house in 1991 for £30,000 (see p. 99). It was one of two images sold with copyright and negatives.

£300+

▼ Terry O'Neill took this portrait of Freddie Mercury (15 x 17½in, 39 x 48cm). It was sold with one of Keith Moon, without copyright.

£200-300 pair

◀ Although this photograph of Jimi Hendrix performing at the Albert Hall in London in 1969 has been taken by an amateur it is a wonderful image of the star. In it Hendrix is using the guitar which was later to fetch a record £198,000 at auction (see p. 99). It was offered for sale with a further twenty unpublished images of Hendrix and Noel Redding, with copyright.

£14,000+ the set

▶ Even images of John Lennon as a boy are avidly sought-after. This Quarry Bank School photograph from May 1957 shows John at the age of 16, already sporting a "teddy boy" hair-cut. Several examples have appeared on the market recently. A signed school photograph of Paul McCart-ney has also appeared at auction (see p. 13).

£200-300

▲ ▲ These two pictures of The Beatles shown above, help to illustrate the difference in value of photographs of the band taken at the beginning and end of their career. The picture (above top), part of a set of 36 black and white photographs (4¼ x 3in, 11 x 7.5cm), shows the band during their first performance at the Odd Spot Club in Liverpool on 29 March 1962. At this time Ringo Starr had not yet replaced Pete

Best as drummer – Starr joined The Beatles in August 1962. Although the image is not very clear, it is an evocative early record of the group. The second photograph is one of a set of 26 shots (6 x 4in, 15 x 10cm) that were taken in April 1969 in one of the band's last formal photo sessions. The pictures were taken by the side of the River Thames in Richmond, London, while Ringo was filming for *The Magic Christian* in nearby Putney.

Early £8,000-9,000

Later £2,000-3,000

Art

Few rock and roll stars have created significant works of visual art, with the notable exception of John Lennon who has worked in a variety of media, and has produced a prodigious quantity of drawings (see pp. 44-47). A number of works of art do come up for sale by artists who have been inspired by various rock and roll stars or their music. Psychedelia was a product of sixties culture (see pp. 118-121) and the pop art movement was largely inspired by Andy Warhol. Rock and pop-related art appeals to both the collector of rock and roll memorabilia and to the modern art collector, and prices for the best examples echo those for mainstream works of art.

◄ Sam Walsh produced this oil on masonite portrait of Paul McCartney entitled *Mike's Brother*. It was exhibited at the City of Bradford Art Gallery in 1964 and the Walker Art Gallery, Liverpool. It is a large piece (64 x 61 in, 162.5 x 155cm) and the image of Paul will appeal to many Beatles' fans. Walsh moved to Liverpool from Ireland in the late 1950s.

£3,000+

▲ *Summer Painting* by Stuart Sutcliffe (71½ x 48in, 182 x 122cm), is important as its sale in 1960 led to Sutcliffe buying a bass guitar and joining The Beatles (see p. 99. It is in oil and plaster on board and has been signed "Stuart 59". It was selected for the John Moores exhibition at the Walker Art Gallery in Liverpool which ran between November 1959 and January 1960.

£7,000+

▼ John Somerville specializes in rock and pop-related art and has made a number of bronze busts of pop stars, including Keith Richards and David Bowie, and special commissions for the Hard Rock Café in the United States. This bronze bust of Mick Jagger (35in, 88cm high) was made in 1984 and is number four in a limited edition of only nine.

£1,500-2,000

▶ Only 300 sets of John Lennon's *Bag One* lithographs were made, with 13 images and a poem celebrating his marriage to Yoko Ono, numbered and signed by him in pencil in 1970. They were sold at the London Arts Gallery for £40 an image, or £540 a set. Some are erotic and the gallery was accused of displaying obscene material (the case was dismissed). Complete sets are rare but individual images come up for sale quite regularly; the erotic images fetch the highest prices.

£9,000-10,000 a set

▲ John Lennon's art has in recent years fetched exceptionally high prices when sold at auction; this collage (8 x 14in, 20 x 35.5cm) sold for £23,000 at a London auction in 1990, a price which was five times the estimated value. The title *Benny and the Jets* is taken from an Elton John single. The piece is made even more desirable because Lennon has signed and dated it in black ink, 1 October 1974.

► David Oxtoby is synonymous with rock and roll art and is widely collected by fans today. This aquatechnique on canvas portrait of Elton John, *Bernie's Mate . . . Elton John,* (30 x 25in, 76.2 x 63.5cm) was exhibited at the Redfern Gallery in 1977. It is signed, titled and dated, and the fact that it was the personal property of Elton John and was sold by him adds to its value.

£6,000+

▲ David Oxtoby produced many portraits in different media, including some engravings in the 1970s. This 1980 portrait of Elvis (40in x 30in, 101.6 x 76.2cm) is signed, dated and numbered 22 of 200; like much Elvis material it is relatively inexpensive.

£200-300

◄ This is one of a number of original pencil portraits of famous rock and pop stars drawn by Cecil Beaton from the private collection of Miss E. Hose. Beaton took his images from the British television programme *Ready! Steady! Go!* which was at the forefront of television pop broadcasting in the 1960s. Although unsigned the portraits are all, like this example of Mick Jagger (7½ x 5¼in, 19 x 13.5cm), stamped with Beaton's name.

£550-650

▶ The Who's lighting engineer John Wolff (Wiggy) commissioned a series of leaded stained glass panels based on the band's album sleeves, to be hung on the walls of the studios. Only two sets were originally produced and a number were sold by John Entwistle in 1988. This example is one of the second set and is based on the cover for the album *Odds And Sods*.

£1,500-2,000

▼ Patti Smith produced this artwork (30 x 22in, 75 x 56cm) at the infamous Chelsea Hotel in New York in September 1969, a year before she became actively involved in rock and roll. It is possibly an idea for an album sleeve, although it was not used.

£600-800

▶ John Lennon's death inspired a number of artists to produce memorial pieces. This bronze bust of Lennon by K. Carter (15½in, 39.5cm high) was exhibited at the Royal Academy in London in 1981. Set on a marble base, it shows Lennon wearing his trademark glasses.

£3,000-4,000

Unsigned Concert Material

Concert programmes, tickets and handbills are usually produced in large quantities and if they are not signed there has to be something particularly notable about them to make them valuable. Most are sold through second-hand shops or by specialist dealers, and in recent years record fairs have become popular outlets for selling mass-produced memorabilia which would not be sold at auction. Scarcity and condition are the most important factors in determining the price. The Beatles command the highest prices and even some mass-produced material for the group can be valuable. Auction houses tend not to sell unsigned Beatles' programmes unless they are in a collection of around 30 when they may provide an interesting historical record.

▲ This set of eight unused tickets is for The Beatles' performance at Suffolk Downs Racetrack, East Boston, Massachusetts on 18 August 1966, only a week before their final public performance, at Candlestick Park. The tickets are mounted with a photograph of the group at the concert, one of their most unusual venues. Tickets are very rarely sold on their own; these particular examples were sold together with a reel of 16mm film for *The Beatles Cartoon Show* (without copyright).

£200-300 the set

◄ Any handbills complete with their original tear-off section are extremely rare and sought-after. This bill for The Beatles' concert at the Odeon Theatre, Llandudno, Wales in 1963 has been mounted together with some other interesting concert material, including some unusual publicity cards.

£250-300

▼ Any ticket from The Beatles' early years before they were famous is particularly collectable. Later on when they were touring cinemas the tickets were less elaborate, whereas earlier ones tend to have more details about the band. This ticket is for Rory Storm's birthday

night celebrations at the Tower Ballroom, New Brighton on 21 September 1962, where The Beatles were making a guest appearance. It was only a month after Ringo Starr had left Rory Storm to join The Beatles, and this gives the ticket added appeal. For display purposes this example has been mounted with a picture of Rory Storm together with Paul, John and George.

£400

▼ Handbills for Jimi Hendrix's US concerts are scarce in the United Kingdom. This bill for his appearance at the Newport Festival is in good condition which adds to its value. An identical bill sold in the United States would fetch far less.

£80-120

▲ Bob Dylan's legendary status ensures that items connected with him command high prices. Such early programmes as this one for his UK tour in 1966 are rare; the fact that it is in excellent condition adds to its value.

£140-160

▲ Very few concert tickets are collectable on their own. However, this unused ticket for the Woodstock festival in New York in 1969 is desirable because it is for a landmark concert which featured great rock and roll legends including Jimi Hendrix and The Who. Although these tickets appear for sale quite regularly in the United States they are rarer in the United Kingdom and the price is affected accordingly. For display purposes the ticket has been mounted with a reproduction of the poster designed for the concert by Arnold Skolnick – originals of the poster sometimes appear for sale.

£250-300

Unsigned Promotional Material

Unsigned promotional material, like unsigned concert material, was usually mass-produced and is of little intrinsic value. It was designed to have a short shelf-life and was disposed of after the advertized event had taken place. Most items survive by chance, although some were collected as mementoes and souvenirs. Unless the material is promoting a significant artist, record or event, value is likely to be nominal and it will usually be sold at second-hand shops and fairs. Such items however, do provide an interesting and colourful collecting area for the more modest pocket.

▼ The monumental influence The Beatles had on every aspect of life is evident in this rare poster advertizing a "Ringo Roll" which was produced by the Sunblest Bakeries on Merseyside in 1963 to honour the band. This particular example, sold at a leading London auction house in 1993, is the only known example to have been offered for sale. It was in pristine condition, but this will have little effect on the value of something so rare. A wrapper for the bread roll has also been offered for sale in recent years. **£600-700**

Top of the "Eat Parade" RINGO ROLL NOW ON SALE AT YOUR LOCAL SUNBLEST AGENTS

▼ The Quarry Men is one of the early names The Beatles performed under between 1957 and 1958. John Lennon was playing with the band when he met Paul McCartney and he was so

impressed that McCartney could tune his guitar himself that he asked him to join the group. This business card for the Quarry Men is extremely rare – only three other examples have been sold at auction in London in the past ten years, and although the corner has been burnt this will have little effect on the price of such an unusual and valuable item.

◄ Posters for Beatles' films often come up for sale. Condition is crucial; major damage will make a poster worthless. Rare examples command a premium; this German poster for *Help!* is worth three times as much as the British poster for the same film.

£250-300   **£300-400**

▲ Promotional material became more sophisticated in the 1970s. EMI sent out limited editions of this clock to retailers and radio stations to advertize Queen's album *News Of The World* in 1977. The design, from the album sleeve, is instantly recognizable. This was one of ten offered as prizes in a competition held by Boots the chemist in 1978. **£200-250**

▼ This silver-coloured ring was issued in a limited edition to promote Keith Richards' solo album *Talk Is Cheap* (1988). **£280-320**

▼ Jamie Reid designed these streamers for The Sex Pistols' film *The Great Rock 'n' Roll Swindle*. He has signed this set of six at a later date. **£300-400**

▼ Promotional leaflets for John Lennon's and Yoko Ono's music, released by Apple in large quantities, are attractive and inexpensive items for the collector today. **£15-20**

Concert Posters

In common with other promotional material, concert posters were designed to be effective for a limited period only, after which time they were usually thrown away. Consequently, few from the 1960s, for example, have survived, and any that do come on the market can fetch very high prices. The rarity of the poster is more important than the condition, and the value will not be greatly affected if the poster is torn or creased; most have lines down the centre where they have been folded up for storage. Those designed in the 1960s were generally very basic, produced by a local printer with just simple graphics. The most sought-after posters are those for big name bands such as The Beatles and The Rolling Stones; those with innovative designs, like those produced by Rick Griffin in the United States; and those for rare concerts, such as performances in small towns. Very early Beatles' posters are particularly rare. Posters are good collectors pieces as they are attractive and easy to display, and they are of historical interest as they state the date and place of a particular performance.

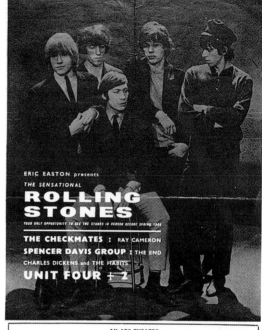

▲ English concert posters for The Rolling Stones are surprisingly rare considering that in the early days the group performed incessantly throughout the United Kingdom. Any that survive have done so by luck (for example, printer's samples or those kept by the manager of the venue as a souvenir). **£500**

◀ Among the earliest posters made for The Beatles are the hand-painted posters for their concerts at the Casbah Club in 1961, designed to be put up on the walls of the club.

£2,200

◀ This is possibly the only example of this poster to have survived for this Beatles' concert in Widnes. Ringo Starr had only just joined the band and his old band, Rory Storm, supported this concert. Of interest are the initials NEMS in the corner of the poster, which refer to Brian Epstein's company, and the name of Bob Wooler, a disc jockey at the Cavern Club.

£3,000+

▲ Concert posters for The Who's early performances are particularly rare and desirable, and although this German poster for The Who's tour in 1966 is graphically simple and has no images of the band, it is still highly collectable.

£700-800

▶ In the 1960s Germany was a country toured by many British groups, including The Rolling Stones, The Beatles and The Who. The image on this poster for The Stones' performance at the Bremen-Stadthalle on March 29th 1967 is striking. Although the poster is not in very good condition and the fact that it is advertising a German tour is not at first evident, it is still very desirable because the name and image of the group is prominent.

£1,500-1,700

◀ Although a number of Jimi Hendrix poster designs have appeared at auction, this particular example for a Jimi Hendrix Experience concert at the Milwaukee Auditorium, United States, on 1 May 1970 is very rare. The design captures the contemporary graphics and concentrates on the image of the star, who is famous enough to be recognized without making a feature of his name. This is rare on such early posters.

£2,200

◀ The design of this poster for Jerry Lee Lewis' performance at the Tower Ballroom in May 1962 is very innovative for its time. The Tower Ballroom was an important Merseyside venue in the 1960s, and in addition to all the local groups who visited, many stars from the United States, including Little Richard, also performed there.

£700

▲ This is an extremely early and rare poster for The Beatles' performance on the Mersey Ferry alongside Acker Bilk and his jazz band. The event was sponsored by the Cavern Club, which at this date was still presenting jazz rather than rock and roll. The poster is hand-painted rather than printed which adds to its desirability.

£3,000

◀ Promoting The Beatles' appearance at the Tower Ballroom in New Brighton in 1963, this poster is far more colourful than the one below left. This time the band are performing with Gerry and The Pacemakers. With a strong design featuring several important names in rock and roll it is an attractive display piece. The slight damage seen in the left hand corner can be hidden by a frame.

£1,200-1,500

▼ Frank Zappa's unique and enigmatic brand of music came to the fore in the 1960s. He has a limited following among collectors, and few items associated with him have appeared on the market. This concert poster for Zappa's performance at the Rheinhalle in Düsseldorf on 23 November 1971 may appeal to a wider group of collectors due to the fine condition and the attractive graphics.

£500

▼ Posters from The Beatles' early performances before they were famous are particularly desirable because they provide an interesting measure of the band's rise to fame and are of nostalgic value. This poster is for the band's appearance at Abergavenny Town Hall Ballroom, only five months before their Royal Command Performance which launched "Beatlemania". The admission price at this early stage in their careers was only 12/6!

£600-800

Beatles Toys and Dolls

The massive success of The Beatles inspired a plethora of inexpensive souvenir material which included a wide variety of dolls. Value depends on rarity because most were made in large quantities. Generally they are relatively inexpensive with only the most exceptional commanding high prices. Condition is very important, and those in mint condition and still in their original boxes are the most desirable. Because much of this material is still available there is plenty of scope for the collector and it is a fun area for those with a limited amount of money to spend.

▲ Selcol "New Beat" Ringo Starr drum kits are far rarer than the guitars (opposite) as there was a smaller demand (most Beatles' fans were inspired to play the guitar rather than drums).

£300-350

▼ These German-made porcelain dolls of The Beatles as they appeared in the *Yellow Submarine* film are very rarely found in a complete set, and even though there is some damage they are still extremely valuable. Single figures also appear on the market. If this set were in perfect condition, each figure would probably command a price of around a third as much again.

£2,500-3,000

◄ Although a number of sets of "Bobb'n Head" Beatles dolls were made by Car Mascots Inc., this set from 1964 is exceptional. At 14in (41cm) high the dolls are far taller than the normal retail variety which stood at only 8in (20cm), and the set was intended for a window display. A supporting letter states that it was presented to John Lennon by the South Milwaukee Beatles' fan club. The motor operating the spring floor of the stage and the lights no longer work, but the size, detail and rarity of this set make it one of the most collectable toys in the field of rock and pop memorabilia.

£3,500

▼ The image used for this 800-piece jigsaw is based on Alan Aldridge's illustrations in the Beatles' book entitled *Beatles Illustrated Lyrics* (1969). The jigsaws were sold together with a full-size colour poster of the band. It is essential that jigsaws are in good condition and particularly that none of the pieces are missing.

£40-60

▼ **Because so many examples of this die-cast Corgi model of the Yellow Submarine were made, only exceptional examples are collectable. This one is in pristine condition and is still in its original box.**

£200+

▲ **This set of Beatles rag dolls dressed in *Sergeant Pepper's Lonely Hearts Club Band* costumes and complete with a cardboard stage and painted metal stands are representative of the type of product The Beatles inspired. Because they are quite large (22in, 55cm high) and in good condition they are collectable, but perhaps not to everyone's taste!**

£100-200

▼ Selcol made reproductions of musical instruments played by The Beatles and The Rolling Stones. This "New Beat" guitar is fairly common, but it is rare to find a set such as this, complete with its original box, instructions and song chart.

£300+

137

Film and Animation

There have been few animated films of rock and pop, and The Beatles' *Yellow Submarine* (1968) is probably the best-known. Original celluloids (cels) from the film regularly appear at auction. Most collectable are those featuring one or more Beatle. Price tends to depend on how many of the band are shown and how big they are. Backgrounds are rare – it is exceptional to find a celluloid of a Beatle with a background. Celluloids from Pink Floyd's *The Wall* (1982) also appear for sale. Stage props and clothing from commercially successful films such as *A Hard Day's Night* and those starring Elvis Presley appear on the market, but these are much less common.

▼ A widely-publicized, specialized sale of artwork from Pink Floyd's film *The Wall* was held in London in 1990. This particular multi-cel set up, entitled *Ranks Of Hammers Goosestepping In Formation*, has been applied to a water-colour and airbrush production background. It is a very large image (14 x 27in/35 x 68cm) and combines a production background with several layers of celluoid. Many other items in the sale were much simpler and fetched lower prices (any with backgrounds always command a premium).

£6,000-7,000

▲ Even though this cel of John Lennon is only three-quarter length it is still expensive because he is the most collectable Beatle.

£400

▲ This rare John Lennon handwritten shooting script for the promotional film for *Hello Goodbye* is a good record of Lennon's hand-writing. It is also annotated with his cartoons and has three parts in George Harrison's hand.

£3,500

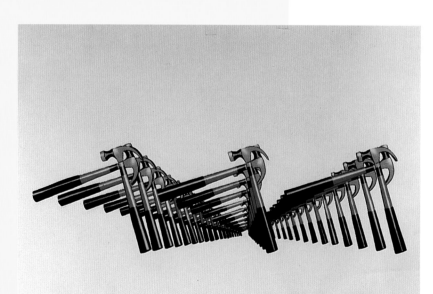

▶ Among the rare examples of rock and pop film props which come on the market is this electric lamp used in The Beatles' film *Help!* in 1965. Originally sprayed in gold paint and used in the Indian restaurant scenes, it has now been painted in white (although the inside still retains the original paint). The lamp is collectable and practical. Provenance is important: it came from the collection of the late Mal Evans, the band's former road manager.

£900

◀ It is rare to find all four members of The Beatles together on one celluloid, and the fact that they are all in full length in this example from *Yellow Submarine* makes it highly desirable. *Celluloids tend to be hard-wearing, but sometimes there are tears or splits, or damage to the gouache. Size varies considerably with celluloids, and the largest ones are usually the most collectable.

£2,000

▼ Only fractions of backgrounds tend to come up for sale so this large, complete example in two pieces from the *Yellow Submarine* is particularly collectable. It is even more exceptional because it also includes a celluloid of some Pepperlanders.

£3,500-4,000

▼ Far rarer than cels from *Yellow Submarine* is this cel from The Sex Pistols' film, *The Great Rock 'n' Roll Swindle* (1980). The film is based on The Sex Pistol's exploits and is a mixture of film and animation. It shows how to "Get rich quick" by deceiving the

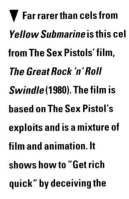

record companies, and was apparently representative of the band's own approach. Examples such as this cel are uncommon. The image of The Sex Pistols as pirates is particularly evocative of the group's ethos, and the portrait of the Queen with a safety pin has come to signify the punk movement. A sticker on the reverse of the cel suggests that this example was used primarily for promotional purposes.

£700-900

Beatles Memorabilia

No other rock and roll band or artist has inspired so many commemorative items as The Beatles. Their great importance is echoed in auction houses and second-hand shops throughout the world, where Beatles-related items quite often occupy up to half of the total stock. A vast range of Beatles souvenirs and memorabilia was produced in late 1963 and early 1964 in both the United Kingdom and the United States. At the other end of the market is a number of one-off items made for The Beatles which are very valuable today.

▲ This tin sign was presented by the Coca-Cola drinks company to the Casbah Club in recognition of the quantities of the drink consumed by the club's patrons. Although there is no mention of The Beatles on the sign the club is such an important part of the band's early career that it still an exceptionally desirable item.

£12,500

◄ This is one of the most publicized rock and pop memorabilia items to have been offered for sale in recent years. Included in the nine scrap albums compiled by a devoted female fan between 1963 and 1969, is a piece of toast taken from George Harrison's breakfast table in 1963, a jelly baby, a twig from a hedge, a cigarette end, and a sock given by George's mother. Usually a scrap album is of nominal value, but the fanaticism evident in this collection makes it a fascinating piece.

£1,200

▲ Among the items exploiting the fame of The Beatles is this coffee table with five tiles featuring the band incorporated into the top. Although the single tiles were widely available commercially it is likely that this table was a one-off design. It is an example of a typical 1960s piece of utility furniture which has been made into a souvenir and is thus a collectable item. **£150-200**

▼ In the United States everyday coin-operated bubble gum machines were inserted with a signed reproduction photograph of The Beatles in an attempt to capitalize on the Beatlemania boom. Examples of these particular piecesrarely appear for sale in the United Kingdom.

◀ The *Mersey Beat* was a local Merseyside music magazine published in the 1960s. This particular edition, from 4 January 1962, is the most collectable as on the front cover it features The Beatles as the top group in a local readers' poll. **£750-1,500**

▼ Although this painted sign for the Cavern Club did not hang outside the building when The Beatles performed there in the early 1960s, it is still highly collectable because of the band's association with the Club, and its fame as a rock venue. **£7,000-8,000**

Other commercially-produced items inspired by The Beatles include plastic brooches, pocket watches, promotional sunglasses, and a series of chewing gum cards.

£150-200

◀ Because these Beatles' Worcester Ware trays were mass-produced and are not difficult to find today, only those in excellent condition such as this example will be collectable. Most are badly worn and scratched and are worth only a few pounds. *Inexpensive Beatles' crockery was also produced in quantity by the Washington Pottery Company. This had a white background and was transfer-printed with a standard design of blue and black figures of The Beatles together with their facsimile signatures. Even if a piece of this crockery is in good condition it is only of nominal value. A complete set is rare and far more collectable. Among the most commonly found pieces are mugs, bowls, plates and saucers.

£40-60 (tray); £10 (crockery)

▶ One of the least expensive Beatles items is this oversized 15in (39cm) plastic comb with a paper strip printed with the usual Beatles' faces and signatures. Few seem to have survived today. **£20-30**

◀ Rolls of wallpaper printed with The Beatles' portraits are common, which suggests that although much was made it did not sell well. Only this one design in these colours was produced. Usually one or two rolls appear together, although occasionally as many as 12 have been sold – enough to decorate a room! Condition is often quite poor, with tears and fading, and as the paper is generally bought for display purposes this will greatly affect value.

£60-80

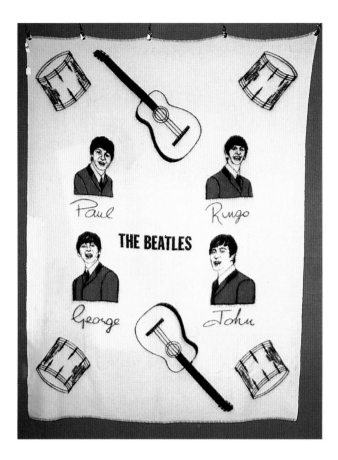

◄ A fan's room could be completely furnished with items bearing images of The Beatles. As people recognize the potential value of Beatles-related items more and more examples are appearing on the market. The increasing supply of this particular blanket, made by Witney Blankets in Oxford with only this one Beatles' design, means that in recent years value has fallen significantly. Again, condition is of paramount importance.

£50-70

▼ The portraits and facsimile signatures on this table lamp were reproduced on many items. Although mass-produced and inexpensive when made, these lamps command relatively high prices today.

£140-160

► This woollen rug woven with the popular images of The Beatles' heads and their instruments was made in Belgium in 1964 and is quite rare to find today. It comes in a relatively large size (36 x 21½ in/ 90 x 57cm) and in good condition with bright colours, it will be sought-after because it is a good item to display.

£120-160

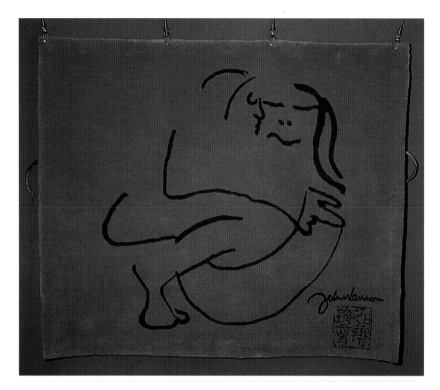

◀ This Bag One rug was made by Marigold Enterprises Limited in the United States in a limited edition of 50, of which this is number 48. It formed part of a set of three designs in three colours, 56 x 46in (1.42 x 1.17m) in size, specially made for the John Lennon exhibition, *The Art of John Lennon*, held around the world in 1988/9. In London the rugs were displayed and sold at the Business Design Centre in Islington. The John and Yoko logo is known all over the world.

£300+

▼ As part of their peace campaign in 1969 John Lennon and Yoko Ono sent a pair of acorns to heads of state throughout the world, with a message inside saying "grow two oak trees for world peace". This unopened box still has the original label, addressed to "His Beatitude Archbishop Makarios President Republic of Cyprus" and is the only example in this condition to have appeared on the market. **£1,200-1,500**

◀ Only signed editions of John Lennon's books are valuable (see pp. 20-21). His first book of poetry, humour and cartoons, *In His Own Write*, was published in March 1964 and was reprinted three times in two months. Signed first editions are the most sought-after, and command the highest prices. If the book is not signed only first editions in pristine condition are worth collecting (these generally cost between £20 and £30). Any other unsigned examples in average condition like this example are abundant, and are relatively easy to find in second-hand or specialist book shops, worth around half the value of a signed piece. This is an interesting and entertaining item for the Beatles collector.

£10-30

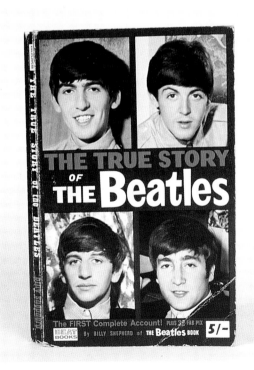

◀ *The Beatles, The Authorized Biography*, by Hunter Davies was the first such book on the band. Published in hardback by Heinemann in 1968, it was published in paperback in 1971. Other than signed copies, only the first edition in good condition with its dust jacket is of any value.

£30-40

▼ A highly unusual rock and roll collectable is this double-decker bus used by Paul McCartney and Wings during the band's Wings Over Europe tour in 1972. Built by the Bristol Bus Company in 1953, it was later customized for Paul McCartney. It had a hi-fi system and a bar installed, and was converted into an open top

◀ Billy Shepherd's paperback book on The Beatles published by Bantam in 1964, regularly appears for sale in second-hand book shops for only a few pounds. This particular book has generally survived in poor condition because it was badly bound, and pages are frequently missing. A copy in pristine condition could therefore be worth significantly more.

£20-30

vehicle for the band's travels throughout Europe. The bus was recently found stored in a garage covered with red paint, and was identified by its registration number. Refurbished to the original design and still in good working order, together with some of its original seats and other features, the bus is a highly individual piece of rock and roll memorabilia, on which it is extremely difficult to place a value.

Biographies

The Beatles (1957-1970)

When schoolboy John Lennon asked Paul McCartney to join his skiffle band The Quarry Men in 1957 he heralded the start of The Beatles. A year later the band were joined by George Harrison, and in 1960 they formed The Beatles with drummer Pete Best and bass guitarist Stuart Sutcliffe who was at art college with Lennon in the 1950s. The band started their career playing in Liverpool clubs and also in Hamburg, Germany. Stuart Sutcliffe left the group at the end of 1960 (and tragically died in 1962) and record store owner Brian Epstein became their manager. He did much to improve their image and got the band signed to the EMI label with producer George Martin in June 1962. Epstein replaced Pete Best with Ringo Starr who had previous played with Rory Storm and the Hurricanes, and in this famous set-up The Beatles recorded their first single *Love Me Do* on 11 September 1962. From then on the band shot to fame. Their next single, *Please Please Me* reached number two in the UK charts in January 1963, and their debut album of the same name was number one for 30 weeks, only to be replaced by their second album, *With The Beatles*. By the end of 1963,

"Beatlemania" had affected the whole of Britain, and between then and 1967, the group had 10 successive number one UK singles. By 1964 the band's fame had reached the United States – at one point Beatles singles occupied the top 5 positions in the US charts. The band were awarded MBEs in the Queen's birthday honours list in 1965 in recognition of their contribution to the music industry. In 1966 they stopped touring to produce a number of albums, including *Revolver* (1966) and *Sergeant Pepper's Lonely Hearts Club Band* (1967). The Beatles formed their own record company, Apple Corps, in 1968, and released *Hey Jude* (1968) which sold over six million copies. Following several differences, somewhat acrimoniously, The Beatles split up in the 1970s. However, their music continues to be listened to by millions, and their huge following is reflected in the demand for Beatles memorabilia.

Eric Clapton (1945-present)

Born in Surrey, Eric Clapton started his early career backing various rhythm and blues bands, including The Roosters in 1963. He then joined The Yardbirds, who he helped to success before leaving in 1965 because he felt their music to be straying away from the pure blues he believed in. He joined John Mayall's Bluesbreakers in 1965 where he established himself as one of the greatest guitarists before leaving to form Cream with bass player Jack Bruce and drummer Ginger Baker. The band enjoyed two years of success before they split. Clapton then joined Blind Faith for a short time and played with a number of musicians, including The Beatles, before joining Derek and the Dominos, with whom he recorded his successful album *Layla And Other Assorted Love Songs* in November 1970. Clapton's career was then curbed by a period of drug addiction, but he made a comeback in 1974 with the album *461 Ocean Boulevard*, which reached number one in the US album charts, and number three in Britain. Clapton's career has continued to flourish with the release of many albums including *Behind The Sun* (1985) and *August* (1986), and singles such as *Wonderful Tonight* (1978) and *I Can't Stand It* (1981), which confirm him as one of the greatest white blues guitarists in history.

Bob Dylan (1941-present)

Born Robert Alan Zimmerman in Minnesota in 1941, Dylan soon adopted the name of Welsh poet Dylan Thomas. Influenced by Woody Guthrie, a New York folk singer, his music reflected the folk song blues of the peace protest music of the early 1960s. His idiosyncratic voice and fine harmonica and guitar playing soon earned him a contract with record producer John Hammond, who also signed Billie Holliday. His first album, *Bob Dylan,* was released in March 1962. This

was followed by *The Freewheelin' Bob Dylan* which reached number one in the UK charts, and *The Times They Are A Changin'*. His lyrics are imbued with political messages, and are outspoken in content. Following a motorcycle crash in 1966, Dylan disappeared into virtual reclusivity, from which he wrote many songs recorded with Ronnie Hawkins' group, The Hawk (later called The Band). Albums include the bootleg *The Basement Tapes* and *John Wesley Harding* (1968). Dylan returned to CBS with *Blood On The Tracks* in 1974, and with Roger McGuinn, Joan Baez and many others toured between 1975 and 1976 with the Rolling Thunder Revue. He starred in a number of films, including *Renaldo & Clara, Hearts of Fire,* and *The Last Waltz,* a film of The Band's final show. He converted from Judaism to Christianity in 1978, releasing the "Born Again" albums *Slow Train Coming, Saved* and *Shot Of Love.* His music was widely celebrated on his fiftieth birthday in 1991, and he continues to perform in the United States and the United Kingdom. His lyrics have influenced the greatest songwriters.

Bill Haley (1925-1981)

Bill Haley began his music career playing country music with The Saddlemen. However in 1953 the group renamed themselves The Comets and their music launched rock and roll. When *Rock Around The Clock* was chosen for the opening of the teenage movie *Blackboard Jungle* in 1955 it sold millions both in the United States and the United Kingdom, where, when the film was shown, teenagers danced in the aisles of the cinemas. Following on from the record's success, the band released a string of singles, and in 1955 had nine separate US hits. However, Haley's fame was short-lived, and he was soon surpassed by such great rock and roll stars as Elvis Presley and Chuck Berry. By 1957 he had almost disappeared from the music scene completely. By the time of his death in 1981 his record sales had made him one of the biggest rock stars of all time.

Jimi Hendrix (1942-1970)

Born in Seattle in 1942, Hendrix taught himself the guitar at a very early age, and in his teens was playing for local bands, including the King Kasuals. After a time in the army in 1962, he started a four year tour backing R&B musicians, including Sam Cook and the Isley Brothers. He formed his own band, Jimmy James & the Blue Flames, in June 1966, and whilst playing in Greenwich Village was discovered by Chas Chandler of The Animals who persuaded him to go back to London with him, where together with bassist Noel Redding and drummer Mitch Mitchell he formed The Jimi Hendrix Experience. With his stunning guitar playing he dazzled British audiences. The band's first three singles released in 1967 – *Hey Joe, Purple Haze* and *The Wind Cries Mary* – all reached the top ten in the UK charts. The Experience toured Europe and the UK before appearing at the Monterey Pop Festival in the United States. Their first album, *Are You Experienced?* was released in May 1967, and its blend of psychedelic blues and Dylanesque lyrics,

together with Hendrix's experimentation with his Stratocaster guitar, put it at number two in the UK charts. The band's second album, *Axis, Bold As Love,* was number 5 in the charts the following year. The Experience then spent much of 1968 in the United States, where they released their third successful album, *Electric Ladyland*. By this time Hendrix was having problems with the band, and in 1969 they split, with only Mitchell remaining to play with Hendrix at the Woodstock festival in August 1969. Hendrix continued to produce successful music. He formed the short-lived group, The Band Of Gypsies, with Billy Cox and Buddy Miles, playing New Year concerts at Fillmore East and releasing an album of the same name in 1970. In 1970 he also made an unsuccessful attempt to relaunch The Jimi Hendrix Experience. From his recording studios in New York he released more influential music on his album *Cry Of Love*, but on 18 September 1970 he was found dead in his flat in London having apparently taken an overdose of drugs. His music continues to be published posthumously, and he is still one of the most influential rock guitarists in musical history.

Buddy Holly (1936-1959)

Born in Texas on 7 September 1936, Buddy Holly's music was strongly influenced by Elvis Presley. He began his career recording with Bob Montgomery as the band Bluegrass, producing a sound which combined country and western and rhythm and blues. With drummer Jerry Allison, guitarist Sonny Curtis, and bassist Don Guess (The Three Tunes), Holly released an unsuccessful early version of *That'll Be The Day* (1956). In 1957 he formed The Crickets with Allison and bassist Larry Welborn, and their new version of *That'll Be The Day* hearalded the start of Holly's success when it reached number three in the US charts. This was followed by *Oh Boy* (1957) and *Peggy Sue* (1957). Holly's skill was unmistakable, and in 1958 his tour throughout Europe and Australia made him one of the most popular musicians of the period. He split with The Crickets in 1958 and his music became more balladic, with singles such as *It Doesn't Matter Anymore*. Unfortunately, Buddy Holly's potential was never realized, because on 3 February 1959 he was killed in a plane crash near Mason City, Iowa. However, he left a legacy of highly influential songs which have been covered by, among others, The Beatles and The Hollies.

Michael Jackson (1958-present)

Probably the greatest modern pop phenomenon in the world, Michael Jackson was already a multi-millionaire in his teens. He began his career with his four brothers as The Jackson Five. They signed with Motown in 1969 and had four number one hits in that year. Michael followed a solo career at the same time and his first solo album, *Got To Be There*, was a worldwide success. *Thriller*, released in 1982, was the biggest-selling pop album to date, and has sold over 40 million copies worldwide. A record seven singles from the album reached the top 10 in the US charts.

Bad, released in 1987, was the first album to enter both the UK and US charts at number one. His highly innovative music videos have paved the way for a host of other stars to follow suit – his promotional video for *Bad* was one of the most expensive videos ever made.

Elton John (1947-present)

Elton was born Reginald Kenneth Dwight in London in 1947. He soon developed a skill for playing the piano and gained a place at the Royal College of Music in 1958. After playing with a number of blues bands, Dwight changed his name to Elton John, a title inspired by sax player Elton Dean and blues singer John Baldry. His first single *I've Been Loving You* – written by Bernie Taupin and published by Dick James who also published Beatles' songs – was a failure, and it was not until the release of *Border Song* by MCA Records in 1969 that Elton John gained any success when the single made the US charts. His second album, *Elton John*, released in 1969, was in the US charts for almost a year and the UK charts for three months. Elton John then went on a series of extensive world tours and produced a number of albums, including *Honky Chateau* (1972) and *Goodbye Yellow Brick Road* (1973). From then on Elton John has had a string of successes, including the duet *Don't Go Breaking My Heart* with Kiki Dee, which was his first UK number one hit. With his flamboyant stage clothes and ornate sets, Elton John has come to be seen as one of the greatest rock performers.

John Lennon (1940-1980)

John Lennon had already started his solo career when The Beatles disbanded in 1971. With his second wife Yoko Ono he produced three albums in 1969 – *Two Virgins*, *Life With The Lions* and *Wedding Album* – all of which were of a highly personal and intimate nature. They were accompanied by a number of much-publicized peace campaigns which included the couple's attendance at a press conference in white pillow cases and a series of "bed-ins". Lennon had his first non-Beatle hit with the song *Give Peace A Chance* which he recorded in 1969 with Yoko Ono as The Plastic Ono Band. Following on from this was his 1970 album *John Lennon/Plastic Ono Band*, made whilst Lennon was undergoing a course of primal scream therapy. His album *Imagine* (1975) brought him back to commercial success. Lennon's emigration to the United States in 1972 was met with some unease – his album *Some Time In New York City* caused some contention. He broke with Yoko for an 18-month "lost weekend" during which time he recorded his Rock'n'Roll album with Phil Spector and a number of singles, which apart from *Whatever Gets You Thru The Night* with Elton John which reached number one in the US album charts, met with little success. He returned to Yoko and his son Sean and following a five year period of not writing songs he released the album *Double Fantasy* (1980) the success of which had added poignancy because on December 8 he was assassinated. Following this a number of singles from the album were worldwide hits, including *Just Like Starting Over* which topped the charts both in the United Kingdom and the United States. Lennon has achieved a status never before reached for a pop star and his popularity is kept alive by continual re-releases of his music.

Madonna (1959-present)

Born of Italian parents (Madonna Louisa Ciccone) in Michigan, Madonna began her career as a dancer before becoming a backing singer to French performer Patrick Hernandez. Playing the drums and singing for *The Breakfast Club* she then formed her own band Emmy. Her first chart successes were the transatlantic hits *Holiday* and *Lucky Star* released in 1984 – the first of an unprecedented run of 16 US top 10 singles. In the same year she gained acclaim in the film *Desperately Seeking Susan*. Following this she had her first US number one hit with the single, *Like A Virgin*, and the album of the same name sold over seven million copies in the United States. Her first hit in the United Kingdom was *Into The Groove* which reached number one in the UK charts in 1985. Her music is promoted by striking dance videos, and Madonna is as famous for her performing as her singing. Her success has been unprecedented since Elvis Presley and The Beatles, and she has sold over 80 million albums worldwide.

Elvis Presley (1935-1977)

Born in Mississippi on 8 January 1935, Elvis's musical career began when in 1953 he recorded two songs at the Memphis Recording Service as a present for his mother and his talent was spotted by the entrepreneur of the new Sun record company. After a shaky start, his first three singles *That's All Right Mama*, *Mystery Train* and *Baby Let's Play House* brought him fame, and in 1955 he was signed to RCA Records for the sum of $40,000. With RCA's backing he soon became a massive star, seen by millions on television gyrating his hips and singing rock and roll. By the end of 1960 he had had 14 number one hits in the United States, including *Heartbreak Hotel* (1956), *Hound Dog* (1956) and *Love Me Tender* (1956). In the United Kingdom he was the first music star to have eight simultaneous singles in the UK Top 30 charts, and in 1958 *Jailhouse Rock* became the first record to go straight to number one in the UK charts. In the 1960s he starred in a series of Hollywood musicals each accompanied by a soundtrack album (all of which went gold), but from this time on, although he still had some major hits, his musical appeal faded as younger and more innovative stars appeared on the scene. Indulging in a life of drugs, alcohol and junk food, Elvis's career met an untimely end with his death in 1977. However, his position as the first great rock and roll star ensures he will remain one of the most important figures in the history of popular music.

Prince (1958–present)

Born Prince Rogers Nelson in Minneapolis in June 1958, Prince played with a number of bands including Flyte Tyme before signing a record contract as a solo performer in 1977. His first album *For You* in 1978 was a hit in the US soul charts, but it took the release of several more albums before he became a star. Signed by MTV he made his debut in the semi-auto-biographical film *Purple Rain* (1984). The sound track of the same name sold one million copies the day it was released and over 10 million overall in the US, where it topped the chart for 24 weeks. A list of hits ensued, including *Around The World In A Day* (1985), *Lovesexy* (1988), *Batman* (1989) and *Graffiti Bridge* (1990). Prince is one of the most talented contemporary artists, who writes and produces all his own music, plays a multitude of instruments, and is an outstanding live performer.

Queen (1972–1991)

Queen was formed from the band Smile which had as its members guitarist John May, Tim Staffell, and Roger Taylor. The band broke up in 1970 and Staffell left. His flatmate Freddie Mercury was persuaded to leave his band Wreckage to join the other members of Smile who together with John Deacon became Queen. They released their first – unsuccessful– album, *Queen*, in 1973; this was followed by *Queen II* which reached number five in the UK charts and also topped the US charts. Their third album *Sheer Heart Attack* (1974) also reached the charts, as did the single *Killer Queen*. However, it was their album *A Night At The Opera* which gained them greatest commercial success, reaching number one in the United Kingdom, and number five in the United States. *Bohemian Rhapsody*, the single from the album, was number one in the UK charts for nine weeks at the end of 1975. Following on from this Queen went on to release a number of successful albums includng *A Day At The Races* (1976), *The Game* (1980), *Greatest Hits* (1981), *A Kind Of Magic* (1986) and *The Miracle* (1989) and gained notoriety for their "glam-rock" stage shows, perhaps most notable of which was their performance at Live Aid in 1985. Unfortunately Queen's career was cut short by the death of Freddie Mercury in 1991 and since that time the band have made no more records together. Their success as a UK rock band is reflected in the fact that all their albums have gone gold.

The Rolling Stones (1962-present)

Mick Jagger and Keith Richards met at school, but it was not until 1962 that they formed The Rolling Stones, together with a mutual friend Dick Taylor, Brian Jones, pianist Ian Stewart, and drummer Tony Chapman. They began playing in London clubs in 1962 and were brought to fame when they appeared on a BBC radio session gig. Bill Wyman then replaced Taylor and Charlie Watts replaced Chapman. The band gained many fans during their residency at the Crawdaddy Club in Richmond, London, and were soon managed by Andrew Oldham who took Stewart out of the band. Their first single *Come On* (1963) established the band's bad boy image and soon their albums were topping the US charts. They went to the United States in 1964 and recorded the EP *Five By Five* at Chess Studios in Chicago, which along with their second album, was both a US and UK success. *(I Can't Get No) Satisfaction* (1965) was the first single to get to number one in the US (it was also number

one in the UK). They recorded many covers until under the new management of the American Allen Klein they released *Aftermath* (1966), made up of wholly original material. This was succeeded by *Between The Buttons* (1967), a turbulent record reflecting the band's own troubles of drug offences and jail sentences. Further successes include *Jumping Jack Flash* (1968) which went to number one in the UK charts and number three in the US, and the album *Beggars Banquet*. At this time Brian Jones' drug addiction had escalated, and in 1969 he was found dead in his swimming pool. Mick Taylor from John Mayall's band Bluesbreakers took over as guitarist, and the band's next releases *Honky Tonk Women* (1969) and *Let It Bleed* (1969) were big hits. Further successful records include *Sticky Fingers* (1971) and *Exile On Main Street* (1972). Mick Taylor was replaced by Ron Wood of the Faces in 1974, and since then the band has continued to produced records, with mixed success. Although also performing as solo artists, The Rolling Stones continue to tour with a wide and dedicated following of fans.

The Sex Pistols (1975-1979)

The Sex Pistols were at the heart of punk rock music in the 1970s. Formed by Malcolm McLaren at his vintage clothes shop in Chelsea, London, Let It Rock, the band's final line-up included Johnny Rotten (born Lydon), Sid Vicious (born John Beverley), Paul Cook and Steve Jones. Their short career was marked by outrageous behaviour: they swore and spat during concerts; were fired by EMI and A&M Records; and in 1978 Vicious murdered his girlfriend Nancy Spungen then killed himself. However, their nihilistic attitude inspired a generation, and their records were a great success. Releases include the anarchic single *God Save The Queen* (1977) which reached number two in the UK charts, and the album *Never Mind The Bollocks, Here's The Sex Pistols* (1977), which was a number one UK hit.

The Who (1964-1982)

The Who began their career as the R&B band The Detours, formed by Roger Daltrey and John Entwistle, with Keith Moon on drums and Pete Townshend on guitar. They were launched as Mods by their manager Peter Meaden who re-named the band The High Numbers. Their success was limited and it was not until Kit Lambert re-named the band yet again as The Who and gave them a regular weekly slot in London that they gained success. Their debut single *I Can't Explain* (1965) reached the UK top ten, as did *Anyway, Anyhow, Anywhere*. From then on, the band's lyrics and stage shows became more outrageous, with Pete Townshend in particular gaining a reputation for his guitar-smashing antics. The Who's debut alubm *My Generation* (1965) reached the UK top five, and further successes followed with *Substitute* (1966), *I'm A Boy* (1966), *Happy Jack* (1966) and *Pictures Of Lily* (1967). US fame for the Who came in 1967 when the band performed at the Monterey Festival, and *I Can See For Miles* went to number nine in the US charts. In 1969 Townshend's rock opera *Tommy* was released and the advance single *Pinball*

Wizard reached the top 5 in the UK and the top 20 in the US. The opera was made into a film in 1975, and the accompanying soundtrack was another success (as was *Quadrophenia* (1973), also the soundtrack to a rock opera film). Further successful Who albums include *Odds And Sods* (1974), *The Who By Numbers* (1975) and *Who Are You* (1978). When Keith Moon died of a drug overdose in 1978 the band recruited a new drummer, Kenney Jones, and released an album, *The Kids Are Alright* (1979), but never regained their former position in the UK and US charts. Since the band broke up in 1982 its members have followed solo careers, although with limited success.

Glossary

Acetate A vinyl recording, cut on special equipment, with a metal central core. A studio may make several acetates from a tape as a convenient transportable form for listening to. Acetates of recordings that were never officially released are generally the most valuable.

Amplifier An electronic device used to increase the strength of the current fed into it, used to produce a louder live sound.

Aquatechnique A method of etching copper with acid to produce an effect resembling water-colour.

Bootleg A newly-produced item, usually a recording but sometimes a record sleeve or film footage, which is illegal and has never officially been made available in that form.

Cel/Celluloid A painting of a character or object on a transparent sheet of celluloid, photographed in the making of an animated film.

Cel Set-up A cel or cels combined with or without a background used for animated films.

Counterfeit/Fake A non-original item made to look exactly like the original and intentionally designed to deceive.

Demo A demonstration disc. These are usually official recordings which may contain material not intended to be sold commercially but which have managed to find their way on to the market.

Ephemera Printed matter.

Fanzine A comic-type magazine for supporters of a particular band or artist.

First Pressing/Edition The manufactured first version of a record or book. Changes may occur in the appearance of the label, sleeve or jacket which affect the value.

Fuzz Box A foot pedal used with a guitar to distort the sound, popular in the 1960s.

Handbill A small printed notice for distribution by hand promoting a concert.

In-house Award An independent award presented to a band or artist, usually by the record company.

Playlist A usually hand-written list of the songs to be sung at a concert.

Poor Contrast The effect caused by signing an item on an area so it is difficult to read, often found on fakes.

Production Background A background painting that was photographed and used in the released version of an animated film.

Promo/Promotional Item An item produced officially by a company to promote a new product. It usually refers to promotional records sent out to magazines, radio stations etc. These usually differ from the commercially released version with changes in the label or sleeve or, rarely, the recording itself. Some promos are withdrawn after distribution and that recording never officially released.

Proof A first-version of printed material intended to show the proposed final design/wording.

Provenance The origin or background of a particular item.

Psychedelia A movement which originated in the United States in 1966 and spread to the United Kingdom. It embodied the whole philosophy synonymous with the "flower-power" movement and free love. The music was often inspired by hallucinatory drugs, and the images are always brightly-coloured.

Publicity Cards Small photographs of an artist given out as part of the promotional activities of a record company.

Score The incidental music for a film or play.

Shooting Script A copy of the script for a film to be used by the actors/actresses and technicians involved.

Signer An ordinary guitar which has been signed by a pop star who normally uses that type of guitar but which does not actually belong to him.

Test Pressing/White Label Usually an exact copy of the intended commercial recording. The label will differ from a promotional or released version and may give few details or even have a blank (white) label.

Tremolo A device on an organ, piano or guitar which produces a trembling effect.

Useful Addresses

Sotheby's
34/35 New Bond Street
London
W1A 2AA
Tel: 071 493 8080
Fax: 071 409 3100

Sotheby's New York
1334 York Avenue
New York
NY 10021
USA
Tel: 0101 212 606 7000
Fax: 0101 212 606 7107

Christies South
Kensington
85 Old Brompton Road
London SW7 3LD
Tel: 071 581 7611
Fax: 071 321 3321

Bonhams Chelsea
65-69 Lots Road
London SW10 0RN
Tel: 071 351 7611
Fax 071 351 7754

Richard Wolffers
Auctions Inc
133 Kearny Street
Suite 400
San Francisco
CA 94108
USA
Tel: 0101 415 781 5127
Fax: 0101 415 956 0483

Butterfield and
Butterfield
220 San Bruno Avenue
San Francisco
CA 94103
USA
Tel: 0101 415 861 7500
Fax: 0101 415 861 8951

and
Butterfield and
Butterfield
7601 Sunset Boulevard
Los Angeles
CA 90046
Tel 0101 213 850 7500
Fax: 0101 213 850 5843

Record Collector
43-45 St Mary's Road
Ealing
London
W5 5RQ

The Beatles Book
45 St Mary's Road
Ealing
London
W5 5RQ

Bibliography

Cox, Perry, & Lindsay, Joe, *The Beatles Price Guide For American Records*, Third edition, Perry Cox Ent./BIOdisc, 1990 (for a highly detailed and informative discussion by Frank Caiazzo on Beatles' autographs)

Fenick, Barbara, *Collecting The Beatles, Volume 2, An Introduction & Price Guide to Fab Four Collectibles, Records and Memorabilia*, Pierian Press, 1985

Fox, Alison, *Rock & Pop, Phillips Collectors Guides*, Boxtree , 1988

Heatley, Michael, ed, *Virgin Encyclopaedia of Rock*, Virgin Books, 1993

Kay, Hilary, *Rock'n'Roll Collectables*, Pyramid Books, 1992

Lewisohn, Mark, *The Complete Beatles Chronicle*, Pyramid Books, 1992

Record Collector, *Rare Record Price Gude 1994*, Diamond Publishing Group Ltd, 1994

Tobler, John, *NME Who's Who in Rock and Roll*, Hamlyn, 1991

Index

Acknowledgments

The publishers would like to thank the following auction houses,
museums, dealers, collectors and other sources for supplying pictures for use in this book
or for allowing their pieces to be photographed.

jkt back tMainman S.A./Jones Music and Isolar Enterprises, Inc. 10tl B/CSK; 11SL; 12 t©Apple Corps Ltd./Dezo Hoffman, cCSK/IB, b©Apple Corps Ltd./Walter Shenson Films; 13tlCSK; trCSk, brSL; 14tSL, bSL; 15tlSL, trCSK/IB, blSL; 16tCSK/IB, b©Apple Corps Ltd./Dezo Hoffman; 17tSL/IB, blCSK/IB, br©Apple Corps Ltd./Dezo Hoffman; 18tSL, bSL; 19tlSL, trCSK, bCSK/IB; 20tSL, b©1994 The Andy Warhol Foundation for the Visual Arts, Inc.; 21tlSL, trSL/IB, cCSK/IB, bSL/IB; 22tSL/IB, blSL/IB, brSL/IB; 23tlSL/IB, trSL/IB, bl©1994 The Andy Warhol Foundation for the Visual Arts, Inc., brSL; 24tlSL/IB, trCSK/IB, bSL/IB; 25tlCSK/IB, r©Apple Corps Ltd., blCSK/IB; 26tCSK/IB, bSL/IB; 27tlCSK, tr©Apple Corps Ltd./Whitaker, c©Apple Corps Ltd./Dezo Hoffman, bCSK/IB; 28tPeter Blake/Waddington Galleries Ltd., clSL, bSL/IB; 29tCSK/IB, clCSK/IB, blSL/IB; 30tSL, blSL/IB; 31tCSK/IB, clCSK, crSNY, bCSK; 32tSL, cCSK, bCSK; 33tlSL, trSL, cSL, bSL/IB; 34tSl/IB, bCsk/IB; 35tSL, cSL/IB, bCSK/IB; 36tCSK, bSL; 37tSL/IB, blSL, brCSK/IB; 38tCSK/IB, bSL/IB; 39tSL/IB, clCSK/IB, crSL/IB, bSL; 40tPL, bCSK/IB; 41tCSK, clCSK/IB, crSL/IB, bCSK/IB; 42tlCSK, trSL, bCSK; 43tlCSK/IB, cSL/IB, bSL/I B; 44CSK; 45tCSK/IB, cSL/IB, br©Pauline Sutcliffe; 46tSL, crCSK/IB, bPCSK; 47trCSK/IB, clSL, bCSK; 48tPL, bSL; 49trSL, blSNY, brCSK/IB; 50tSL/IB; c©Apple Corps Ltd., bSL/IB; 51tSL, crSL/IB, blPaul Wane; 52tl"Elvis and Elvis Presley are Registered Trademarks of Elvis Presley Enterprises, Inc." ©1994, trSL/IB, bCSK/IB; 53tlSL/IB, trSL/IB, bWalter Shenson Films; 54tSL, blCSK, brSL; 55tlSL, trCSK/IB, blCSK, brCSK/IB; 56tlCSK,; 57©1994 The Andy Warhol Foundation for the Visual Arts, Inc.; 58tCSK, bSL; 59tCSK/IB, blSL, brSL; 60tSL, cCSK/IB, bCSK; 61tSL/IB, blSL/IB, brSL/IB; 62tlCSK/IB, blSL, rCSK/IB; 63tlCSK, cCSK/IB; bCSK/IB; 64tCSK/IB, bCSK/IB,; 65tlSL/IB, trCSK/IB, bl SL, brSL; 66tCSK, bCSK/IB; 67tPL, cSL/IB, bCSK/IB; 68tlCSK/IB, trCSK/IB, cSL/IB, brSL/IB; 69tCSK, cCSK/IB; bSL/IB; 70tSL/IB, bCSK/IB; 71tlCSK/IB, tr©Apple Corps Ltd., blCSK/IB, brCSK/IB; 72SL, 73SL; 74tSL, bHub Willson; 75tlCSK, trSL/IB, blSL/IB, brHub Willson; 76tSL, blCSK/IB, brCSK/IB; 77tSL, blCSK, brCSK; 78tCSK/IB, bl CSK, brCSK; 79tlSL, trCSK, bHub Wilson; 80SL, trSNY, bCSK; 81tPL, cCSK/IB, bSNY; 82tSL, blSL, brSL; 83tlSL, trSL, bSL; 84trCSK/IB, bSL; 85trCSK, cCSK/IB, brCSK; 86tSL, blCSK/IB, brPL; 87tlCSK, trPL, blCSK/IB, brSL; 88tPL, bPL; 89tRCSK, cSL, bl CSK/IB, brSL; 90cCSK, blSL, brCSK; 91tSNY, trCSK, b cSK; 92tSL, blSL; 93tlCSK, cSNY, blCSK/IB, brCSK; 94tSL, blCSK; 95trCSK, cS, blSL/IB, brSL; 96SL; 97SL/IB; 98tSNY, cSNY, brSL; 99tlSL, trSL, cbSL; 100tlSL/IB, trCSK, blSL, brCSK/IB; 101tCSK, bSNY; 102tCSK/IB, blCSK/IB, br CSK/IB; 103tlCSK, trSL/IB, bCSK/IB; 104tSL/IB, cCSK/IB, bSNY; 105tSL/IB, cCSK/IB, blCSK/IB, brSNY; 106tSL, bSL; 107tSL, cSL, blSL, brSNY; 108tSL, blPL, crSL/IB; 109tSL, cSL, blCSK, brSL; 110tCSK/IB, cSL, bCSK/IB; 111tSL, bSL; 112tHub Willson, lSL, bSL; 113tSL, trSL, cSL, bSL; 114CSK/IB; 115 CSK/IB; 116 tSL/IB, bSL; 117tSL, clCSK, crSL, bCSK/IB, 118tCSK, c©1968 Bill Graham #FME 7, Artist: David Byrd; bSL; 119trSL/IB, blMartin Sharp, brMrs N Somerville; 120t©1968 Bill Graham #99, Artist: Bonnie MacLean, bCSK/IB: 121tSL, bPL; 122tPhotograph by Gered Mankowitz ©Bowstir Ltd., blSL, brCSK/IB; 123tlCourtesy of The Jimi Hendrix Museum, Seattle, Washington, USA, rSL, blSL; 124t©Pauline Sutcliffe, bCSK; 125tSL, crCSK, bCSK; 126tSL, clDavid Oxtoby, bThe National Portrait Gallery, London; 127tSL/IB, blSL, brSL; 128tCSK/IB, bCSK/IB; 129tCSK/IB, clCSK/IB, cCSK/IB, bCSK/IB; 130cCSK/IB, blCSK/IB, crCSK/IB; 131lCSK/IB, tcCSK/IB, trCSK/IB, bCSK; 132tSL, bSL; 133tlSL, trSL/IB, bSL/IB; 134tlSL/IB, trSL; bSL; 135tlSL; blSL/IB; brSL/IB; 136tCSK/IB, blSL, brCSK/IB; 137tCSK/IB, trCSK/IB, blCSK/IB, BrCSK/IB; 138trSL/IB, cCSK/IB, blCSK; 139tlSL/IB, clSL, crSL/IB, bSL/IB; 140tSL, bSL; 141tSL/IB, cSL/IB, crSCK/IB, bSL; 142tSL/IB, cCSK/IB, bCSK/IB; 143tlCSK/IB, crCSK/IB, bSL; 144trLCSK/IB, cSL/IB, bCSK/IB; 145tlCSK/IB, cSL/IB, bCSK/IB

Key

b bottom, c centre, l left, r right, t top

SL	Sotheby's London	SL/IB	Special photography taken by Ian Booth at Sotheby's
SNY	Sotheby's New York		
CSK	Christie's South Kensington	CSK/IB	Special photography taken by Ian Booth at Christie's South Kensington
PL	Phillips, London		

The Author would like to thank Sotheby's London and New York, Christie's South Kensington, Phillips, Paul Wane, John Bramley, Joe Long, Alison Macfarlane and Carol Greenway.
The Publishers would like to give special thanks to Carey Wallace at Christie's South Kensington.